WAKE UP

2

FORGIVNESS

By

Mary Mag-Dalene

By Mary Mag-Dalene Maxion

Mae*Mae Publishing

ISBN: 978-0-615-57068-6

This is a true biography based on the real life events of my real momma. We are not trying to hurt anyone by telling this story. We are only trying to help others with her story. All the names and some events have been changed to protect everyone's identity.

Photography by: John Bates

www.jbates3@gmail.com

DEDICATION

This book is dedicated to my four lovely flowers, my daughters. I also dedicate this book to my baby boys. I love and miss them very much.

INTRODUCTION

Matthew 18:21–22

"Peter came to Jesus and asked,

'Lord, how many times shall I forgive

my brother when he sins against me?

Up to seven times?' Jesus answered, 'I tell you,

not seven times, but seventy-seven times.'"

She wears a smile on her swollen face. Wishing no one notice's as she sits on the couch at her daughter's house. She is wearing an all black wig on her head with brown highlights. This wasn't any wig, it was her favorite one.

Her eyebrows are drawn in to make her face look as if she remembered it 6 years ago. That was six years ago when her life was cancer free. Her eyes are so puffy and red from all the medication that she has to take every day.

She is attempting to cover her eyes by wearing a pair of thick rimmed-glasses with a brown tint. Her glasses are resting on a swollen nose. The same glasses that she hates to wear, because they will leave a black mark on each side of her nose.

Her cheeks are extra puffy and red. So much so, that it looks as if she has on make-up. She is smiling for the camera. Her lips are turned into a half kool-aid grin that shows her pain.

She wears brown lipstick in hopes of preserving her beauty. Her body is swollen all over. Her neck has wrinkles that resemble a baby's neck. She is wearing a gold chain around her neck that she has had for years.

The chain now hangs down to the crevice of her breast and lays flat. At one time, it would sit out. That was before gravity entered her life.

She is wearing an all black shear dress jacket. It fits kind of snug on her swollen arms. The black silk shirt that she is wearing is sleeveless. On the left side of her chest directly over her heart, she has on a silver flower broche.

She is sitting with her right arm thrown across the end of couch in a lazy way. She is so tired after spending for 5 months in the hospital. Her little eyes can barely stay open.

Her fingernails are painted red. They are the only thing that Chemotherapy could not take away. She is also sitting with her legs crossed, as she waits for the photographer to snap the shot. The red complexion of her skin only adds to her beauty.

The woman that I just described is my real mother Grace Jean Flowers. I have, and will always love her. There were circumstances in her life that prevented her from being there for me. It wasn't that I didn't love my real mother. I just found it hard to love her sometimes.

There was always this void in my heart that I held for her. I just couldn't quite put my finger on it. Not until I found myself taking care of her. I was finally able answer the question.

Do I blame my real momma? My answer is, yes I did. I was angry at myself for getting angry with her. For years, I tried not to accept the fact that I blamed her.

During her sickness, I had to watch her suffer. Each time that I prayed for God to heal her. I believe that God was healing me. The doctor's gave my real momma one year to live, but she lived seven.

Forgiveness was not something that was going to happen overnight. God gave me seven years to learn to forgive my real momma. It seemed like each year that she was here with me. I grew to see her way God saw her.

I held so much hurt and pain inside of me. It came to a point where, I sort of resented her. However, now I would love to tell my real momma that I humbly forgive her.

Luke 7:36-50.....Sinful Women Are Forgiven

"Do you see this woman? I entered your house; you gave me no water for my feet, but she has wet my feet with her tears and wiped them with her hair. [45] You gave me no kiss, but from the time I came in, she has not ceased to kiss my feet. [46] You did not anoint my head with oil, but she has anointed my feet with ointment. [47] Therefore, I tell you, her sins, which are many, are forgiven—for she loved much. But he, who is forgiven little, loves little." And he said to her, "Your sins are forgiven.

CHAPTER ONE

WHY?

"Oh my God!

Oh my God!

Oh my God!

Please don't do this!

God, Please!" I was screaming on the inside. I knew it was wrong, but I did whatever he told me to do. As I lay in bed completely silent, my only form of protest was in my head.

That night when those hands began to rub all on my young body. I didn't know what to do. I couldn't believe what was happening to me. Those familiar hands crept up under my pink nightgown. I just froze immediately.

I was only sixteen years old, and having someone touch me like that, was very creepy, and unnatural. I couldn't run, or scream or he would have beaten me.

"Please God!

Please God!

Please God!

Help me!" I was yelling at God in my head.

I quivered in bed, when hands began to touch my body from every direction. He was running the show, and the other person only went off his instructions. He was a very good manipulator and good at brainwashing anyone.

In his mind, he believed that he had magical powers. Truth was he was just a bully. He bullied everyone involved into participating right now. I was probably the only one, which he was beating.

The other person he just manipulated the crap out of them. As my clothes began to leave my body, every ounce of dignity and self-esteem went with them. There was no intimacy, or preparation involved.

Everything just began to happen at one time.

Both of their lips are kissing me at once, all the while I am dying inside. I was then told, to open my legs.

"No!

No!

No, why me?" I began to panic inside.

I knew that this was wrong. The preacher man didn't have to say too much of anything. He was just that threatening. All he had to do was look at me and I'll be ready to shit my pants. Before I knew what was happening, he pried my legs open.

My real momma began to perform the most embarrassing acts on me. The preacher man began to take off those faded black slacks. He did not drink, so I cannot say that alcohol was the reason to his madness.

This is probably the worst thing that anyone can ask me to recall. I know that I have to tell my story the good, the bad, and the ugly. It's just that, having to remember those acts brings up so much anger inside of me.

"Only God can bring me through this," I began whisper in my head. He was determined to kill my light at any cost. Even if it meant making my own mother have sex with me.

It was like the preacher man and my real momma would have sex. Then, he would make her have sex with me. I don't know what to say, the shit was crazy. My baby would be sleeping in the baby bed, right next to us.

My other momma, well, I could hear her snoring in her own room. Weird thing was that there was a pig that slept in our room.

It was in the fall of 1976, on one of my real mother visits when we lived in Amarelle, Arkansas. The preacher man had already known that my real mother liked girls. People gossiped all the time.

Everyone knew about my real momma. So her liking girls, was absolutely no secret. The preacher man, he had no morals, and me, well I was his property. Who did, whatever he told me to do.

Therefore we all went to bed that night. He made her teach me how to have sex with a woman. I hated it. It was humiliating, and there was nothing enjoyable about the sex act.

I wished that my real mother, would have stood up for me, and said, "No!

No, I will not do those things to my baby!" However, she said nothing. Honestly, she was too scared herself.

Once he was all done with me, I was pushed to the side. I grabbed the sheet and wrapped it around my body. The bed began to squeak next to me, and all I heard was heavy breathing. I cried silently as I dozed off to sleep.

She only stayed for a couple of days or so. I believe that she could not take it anymore. It was like every night we went to bed, or whenever he got horny. He expected for all of us to have sex together. We could not tell him no.

One day my real momma packed her bags, said good-bye, and just walked out the door. It didn't surprise me that my real momma left without me. She had done it so many times before.

Technically, I couldn't blame her one bit. I wanted to get away myself, but I was stuck. I would have left with her when she walked out of the door. My footprints would have been following my real mother's.

She was able to get away. However as for me, I couldn't. I just couldn't walk out that door, because no one would take me in. I was still a child. Therefore the only person that I could call on was God.

I would run outside and stand in the middle of the yard. My arms would be extended out like wings. I would look up to the sky and say, "Why?

Why God?

Why God, did this happen to me?

Why can't anyone help me?" All I ever wanted was to be a kid.

That one night began to become an expected event. One in which the preacher man demanded every time she came to visit. My relationship with my real mother was already strained, but the evil that we experienced almost ruined it.

WHO AM I?

Hello, my name is Linda Kay Flower. I was born on a cold winter night at 11:58pm in Blytheville, Arkansas. The day that I was born on, is a blessing or a curse to most people. My date of birth is December 24, 1958, or Christmas Eve.

There are many people who say that, it's a blessing to be born on Christmas Eve. One thing that I realized was that on my Birthday, I was cheated. People got away with only giving me one gift, which for me was a curse.

I was born to a woman named Grace Flower. My birth mother was only fourteen years old when she conceived me. I don't blame my birth mother, at all for anything I went through. She was just a child herself.

At the time of my birth, my real momma was living in between her female friend's house, and on the streets. Pretty much, my real mother was homeless. She had no support from her own mother, because her mother was also young.

When I turned one year's old, my real mother stole some stuff from a store. The cops arrested her at the age of fifteen. She was sentenced to a reform school for girls.

My real mother did not want her friend to have custody of me. She had to come up with someone to take me in, or they would have put me in a home for kids. My real mother was trying to do the best thing for me.

There was an elderly couple of whom, my birth mother knew. They didn't have any children of their own. So, she arranged for them to keep me. Regardless of the facts, she was trying her best.

You see, in the sixties there was no such thing as adoption. Couple's would raise a child as their own without any government intervention. The couple, she gave me to, were named the Strong's.

I was two years old when my real momma left me with them. Once my birth mother got out of reform school at the age of eighteen, she never took me back. One thing I can say, is that, real momma was always around somewhere in the picture.

The Strong's were a very sweet couple, and they were financially well off. My real mother felt that by sending me to live with the Strong's. I would get to live the life that she was not able to provide for me.

I would not consider myself one of the prettiest girls. When I think back, I can picture myself around the age of six or seven. At an early age, I was horrible looking. I was dark skinned, or red with a very huge tan. Then again, it could have been dirt, because I do not remember taking many baths.

My teeth looked like they belonged to a dog. They were long and sharp, and I was missing one of my two-front teeth. Funny story the way I lost that tooth. It happened when I was in Kindergarten.

I was the tallest one in my class. All of the kids were five years old, but I wasn't. I was six years old, and could barely count. The kids in my first grade class had a list of things to tease me about.

My first grade teacher was Mrs. Henry. Oh, boy was she mean. This lady was tall and skinny. She used to pick on me every day. Mrs. Henry knew that I could barely count.

Therefore every time she would pick someone to count out loud. Her green eyes looked directly at me. I would stand up out of my little brown desk. There were about twenty other kids sitting in the same brown desk with the chair attached.

The desks were lined up in rows of five. Once, I began counting and messed up, they all would burst out laughing. No one would play with me except a girl named Monique, who sat in front of me.

For the first time someone was nice to me. Monique was a pretty girl, and she would always wear her hair in Mickey Mouse ponytails. It was maybe about a month into school. We all had been dismissed for recess.

Monique and I went off to ourselves to play. No one would play with her as long as she played with me. So we began running and playing with each other, until everything went dark.

The last thing that I remembered was Monique and I was head butting each other. Evidently,

Monique's head went into my mouth instead of my head. Hump, I guess I should have held my head down just a little lower.

When I came to, my mouth was pouring blood. All the teachers ran over to where I was crying and holding my bloody mouth. Including Mrs. Henry, she attempted to be concerned. I looked over at Monique who told me she was sorry.

I was taken into the little girl's room. Mrs. Henry leaned me over the metal sink and told me to rinse my mouth out. Once I was done rinsing my mouth out. I ran my tongue over my two front teeth, and my tongue felt an empty spot.

I was so embarrassed. So when my daddy came to pick me up from school that day. I had nothing to smile about. My parents didn't know anything about going to dentist. I now had a permanent missing front tooth.

I also had a mark on my nose that the kids used to tease me about. Kids are definitely cruel. They teased and taunted me all the time. I was called names like foggy doggy or stripy nose. It was bad trust me.

THE STRONG'S

The Strong's were my parents. I called them momma and daddy. They named me Linda Ann Strong. I was treated just like their own flesh and blood. They spoiled me rotten.

Even though, they were not my real parents. I loved them just the same. They were the sweetest people that I ever met. I knew how to get anything that what I wanted from them.

When I think back to that time, it was as if I was living in a fairy tale. I was a carefree child then, without a care in the world. I never would have thought that overnight my life would be turned upside down?

My momma was a very short older woman probably in her late fifties. She was thin with like, brown skin and some long gray hair. The thing about my momma was that she would wear these funny looking wigs.

She was a very firm woman for her size. I would say that my momma was every bit of four feet something. My momma, well she never had problem disciplining me. Whenever I was bad, she tore my butt up.

She was also illiterate and going blind. She was very good at counting money in increments of twenty. Strange thing was that she also knew how to read the Bible. Which was weird to me, because she could not read or write.

Maybe it was from memory, of when she was a child herself. I don't know truthfully. I'm guessing that she attended church religiously when she was young, and the Bible stories stuck in her memory.

I never knew my real father. I would learn things about my alleged father through different family members, here and there. They would say things as if my daddy was actually my real father.

Hearing that would make me smile, because I loved my daddy. They believed that he was my real father, since I looked like him. He was a tall medium built man, probably in his early sixties.

My daddy had some red skin just like me. He always had a baldhead even in the nineteen-sixties. He was a very strong man, who had served in World War 1. He was also illiterate too.

Due to the time my momma and daddy grew up in. They received little to no education. You see, in the South, blacks had very little to no education.

Back then, blacks had to deal with Jim Crow and his friends. Education was hard for blacks to achieve. Therefore, a lot of older blacks never received the opportunity to attend school.

Anyway, he did know how to read and write, but just a little. He was also very good at counting money.

My daddy was a very smart man. He never let anyone get anything over on him.

I was his sweetheart, and I loved him to death. God could not have placed a better man in my life. He was the only father figure that I have ever known.

FIRST WHIPPING

As a child I was bad not terrible. The kids that I grew up around used to play momma and daddy a lot. Where we would pretend to be momma and daddy, and play kiss each other. We were kids just having fun.

We would also play B*Ball. B*Ball was just another name for basket-ball. The difference was that we didn't have a basketball rim, court, or even a gym. We played in dirt fields and used buckets as our hoop. I was somewhat of a tomboy back then.

The kids would still pick on me every day. Even though, they would play with me. I was always the target of their teasing. Actually, the only way that I was able to make any friends, was to bribe them.

My need to buy friends is what led to my first spanking by my daddy. Momma and daddy had money. They both were receiving social security checks. My daddy also received veteran's assistant check.

Back then, my parents would wear what people called money belts. They would have five and six hundred dollars wrapped around their waist at any given time. I would get an allowance at the end of the week or certain days.

For whatever reason, I just cannot, remember why I didn't have any money this particular day. If I can recall it was Friday, the night before the Fourth of July. My bed was still in my momma and daddy's bedroom then.

I knew that they would always sleep with their money at the foot of the bed. My parents were both fast asleep this night and snoring loudly. I needed to buy some things. I needed to bribe the other kids to play with me.

As I listened to them snoring, and was watching momma toss and turn, I made my move. There was no turning back now. I crept out of my bed, tiptoed to the foot of my momma, and daddy's bed. Then, I grabbed my momma's money belt, and opened her money pouch.

I grabbed my momma's belt, because I figured that she would not notice anything missing. Next, I picked up her belt and began counting five's, ten's, and twenty-dollar bills. In my mind, I was imagining all the candy that I was going to be able to buy tomorrow. All I wanted was some friends.

My parents began to move around in the bed, and I got scared. Then my daddy began to snore so loud, that my heart began beating in my chest, like a drum session at a football game. I snatched a twenty-dollar bill, jumped back in my bed, and went to sleep without them even waking up.

On Saturday mornings, we would go shopping. Therefore, this particular Saturday, we woke up, got dressed as normal. Then we prepared for the day.

We went shopping as always. My daddy had to stop off and do a job. He would work construction sometimes for different people fixing things. He was like the Jack-Of-All-Trades. There was nothing my daddy couldn't do.

He parked across the street from a store where his job was. Then he and my momma, got out the car so that daddy could go to work. I was supposed to wait in the car until they returned.

I watched them walk across the street and disappear into a house. I waited a good couple of minutes before I got out the back seat of the car. Then I darted out off into the candy store.

I walked into the store and bought firecrackers, chips, and candy for the kids. My purpose for buying all that stuff was to get the kids to play with me once I got home. I probably only spent about three dollars.

I distinctly remember receiving seventeen dollars in change. As I sat in the backseat and waited for my momma and daddy to return, I began to get nervous. Truth is that it seemed like an eternity before they finally came out of that house.

First, momma entered and sat in the passenger seat. Then, daddy opened the driver's side door and sat behind the steering wheel. My heart was beating uncontrollably, and I begun to breathe very hard. Now, that I think about it, my daddy may have heard me breathing.

Anyway, the next thing I remember, he turned around, and looked directly at my bag of goodies. He looked at me and said, "Buddy, did you give this child some money"? Buddy is what my daddy called my momma.

My momma turned all the way around in her seat, looked directly at me, and said, "No"! My father's, eyes got real big, and he asked me where I got money from. I didn't know what to say, so I said the first thing that came to mind. "Big Cousin gave it to me!"

I knew that my father immediately did not believe me, because he knew that Big Cousin did not have any money. Hell, even if he did he would not have given me any money.

Big Cousin was like my older foster brother. He was thirty-something years old and always wore a small afro. His eyes were crossed, and he was not very tall. I can remember him being very skinny.

My momma and daddy raised him also. Big Cousin was somewhat mentally disabled, and he would stutter. Even though Big Cousin was nice to me, my daddy knew that I was lying.

My daddy looked at me and said, "Well, if you say Big Cousin gave you this money!

I'll just go and ask him why he is giving you any money?" I almost pissed right there in my pants.

I began to try to think of another lie very quick, but nothing could come to mind. "Buddy, count your money belt!" I heard my daddy say to my momma

Mind you, that my momma is illiterate. She took off her money belt and began counting her money in increments of twenties. "Twenty.

Forty.

Sixty.

Eighty.

One-hundred.

One-hundred and twenty…" Then she stopped. There was no more money in her belt.

My parents always knew how much money they had at all times. Therefore, when my father realized that a twenty-dollar bill was missing, I wanted to die. If I could have jumped out of the back window, I would have.

My daddy grabbed my bag of goodies. He poured everything out onto the backseat. The sparkles, red firecrackers, and my squirrel candy were all in his face. His jaw began twitching as he tore my tail up from the front seat. I would have rather that my momma whipped me.

Next he turned around in the seat, and drove away. I never stole anything else, and never got another whipping from my daddy at least. Receiving a whipping from my daddy was like the ultimate punishment for me, because he had some heavy hands.

CHAPTER TWO

MEMORIES

One of the funniest memories that I have of my dad, was on my fifth birthday. I never was given a birthday party. So I had decided to throw my own party. I had invited all of my dolls.

We were all sitting around my little white play table, in the living room. I was wearing my white Sunday dress that had colorful flowers all over it. My hair was combed and in some pretty pony tails. Even my dolls were dressed for the occasion.

I think that my daddy and momma were getting Christmas dinner ready, or something like that. The smell of greens and corn bread was all over the house. It was one of those cool, windy days. Just, a little unusual for Arkansas. We had the front door open.

Then all of a sudden this pretty brown cat ran onto the porch. I ran outside on the porch and picked the cat up. My thinking was that if I could get the cat in the house, momma and daddy would let me keep it.

Besides, it was my birthday and this cat was now my invited guest. Therefore, I took the cat in the house. Sat back down at the table, and started hugging the cat very tight. I was rocking the cat back and forward, back and forward singing, "Happy Birthday to me."

"Happy Birthday to me!

Happy birthday to me..." I was having a good ole time.

Next thing I know. The cat began squirming and trying to get away. It seemed like, the more he tried to get away. The tighter I held him and I was still singing. "May the good Lord bless me?

May the good Lord bless me?" I literally, had a death grip on the cat.

"May the good Lord bless?

Aagh!

Aagh!" Then all of a sudden, the cat reached up, and scratched me right in my eye.

I mean like, directly in the white part of my eye. The cat went flying across the living room floor. Momma and daddy came running into the room, to see what I have gotten myself into this time. What they saw was me, jumping up and down screaming at the top of my lungs.

The cat ran and hid in the corner. When they saw that it was a cat, my daddy told momma to get a broom. My momma ran back in to the room with the broom, and handed it to my daddy.

This entire time the cat was just sitting in the corner looking for a way out. "Aagh!

Aagh!

Aagh!" I was still screaming and rubbing my eye. My Momma was standing next to me trying to give me some comfort. My daddy began swatting at the cat, and it ran in our bedroom.

Me, momma, and daddy all ran into the room after the cat. It was like a scene out of a cartoon. Daddy started screaming, "Buddy shut the door!

Buddy shut the door!" All I saw was my momma long dress outside of the door. She locked me and daddy, in the bedroom with the cat.

My daddy charged for the cat and it jumped up onto the vanity set. He went to swing for the cat with the broom. Next thing I know, all I saw were claws on his head. I started screaming and crying.

My daddy was turning around in circles trying to get the cat off his head. I ran over and began to beat my daddy on the back, but the cat had his nails into the top of his baldhead.

"Buddy open the door!

Buddy open the door!" My daddy began yelling and running for the door. Before the knob even turned on the door, we all ran out.

"Aagh!

Aagh!" This time my daddy was yelling. The cat was still on his head. My daddy ran out onto the front porch. When he came back in, his head looked like someone scratched it with a metal rake. Needless to say, humph, I could not keep the cat.

CHURCH GROUP

The house that we lived in came from my daddy's own sweat. It was a ranch style house. There was a living room, with a black and white television in it. Our favorite shows were Sanford & Sons and Amos & Andy.

Oh yeah, we had a dining room too. There was only one bedroom that momma, daddy, and I all slept in. They had their own bed and all, but my bed was in front of theirs.

I can remember having a lot of fun with them. Growing up with my parents, was like a dream come true. Food was never an issue for me. Anything that I ever wanted, I got.

One thing about my parents was that, they went to church every Sunday. We would attend both morning and evening services religiously. Shoot, we even attended the services throughout the week and any activities that the church was giving.

You see, my daddy was a Deacon, and my momma always wanted to preach. Actually, she preached at a couple of different churches' here and there. I cannot remember if she was any good, because I never paid any attention during Church Services.

We had our own singing group. For real, my momma, daddy, and I were like a three-man show. Every other Sunday we would sing at different churches.

There was this one particular song, which I just cannot get out of my head.

For the life of me, I cannot remember the name of it. The chorus would go something like, "That's enough!

Hey!

Hey!

That's enough!

Hey!

Hey, that's enough for me!" All I can do is laugh.

I really thought that I could sing. My momma and daddy would be rocking back and forward, clapping, and just a singing. Then I would be standing in the middle of them all off beat.

"Hey!

Hey!

That's enough!

Hey!

Hey!

That's enough for me! See, I told you that I cannot get it out of my head.

MOMMA STRONG

Even though my momma was old, she took very good care of me. However, the one thing she could not do was my hair. She would have people come over to our house and do my hair. All of her fingers were crooked and bent.

The story that I heard was that my momma's marriage to my daddy, was her second one. Rumor has it, that my momma got married at an early age to an older man. The man used to beat her, and was very evil.

One day, my momma's first husband started to beat on her while she was in the kitchen. He picked up a knife and attempted to stab her. Her first husband would regularly abuse her, and she finally fought back.

My momma grabbed the knife with her hand to protect herself. She ended up cutting all of her fingers in order to save her own life. Somehow, after that she got away.

Back then, black people did not go to the doctor for injuries. They would stop the pain with whatever home remedy they knew of. Therefore, my momma never received any medical treatment for her fingers.

When her fingers began to heal, they were crooked. What was weird about her? Was that my butt never knew a difference. Anytime I jumped out of line. My momma was always there to point me back in the right direction.

IRON INCIDENT

I used to have a lot of toys. My momma and daddy bought me everything. One of my favorite toys was an iron and ironing board. I would always see my momma put the real iron on the propane heater, and iron our clothes.

Therefore, this particular day my momma was heating up the real iron. She walked out of the room to do something that I cannot remember. I was always doing something that I shouldn't.

However, I ran over to the iron. I wanted to do what I always saw my momma do. I tried to iron our clothes. The first time, I placed the real iron on my daddy's shirt nothing happened. So I did what my momma always would do.

I put the iron back onto the heater. The iron began to steam and smoke. Everything that I was about to do seemed to make sense at that moment. However, this time I did the stupidest thing ever. I kissed it.

Um...um...um....I actually kissed the iron. Let me tell you, it was hot then. Immediately I pulled the iron away, and began screaming, "Aagh!

Aagh!

Momma, momma, daddy, momma!" Everyone ran back into where I was.

My momma grabbed me, but I was still holding my mouth. My daddy was finally able to pry my mouth open and said, "Buddy, this girl done burned her lips!"

Boy, I tell you.

How'd you do that child? I couldn't talk.

My momma and daddy were like, "What happened to you!" I whispered, "I...kissed the iron.

My lips got stuck." Both of my parents looked at me as if, I had lost my mind. They began laughing until they turned purple.

"It burns!

It burns!

Aagh", was all I could say! My momma pulled me over to the sink, and began running water on my lips. I was so embarrassed, because they kept laughing at me.

Pretty much, for the rest of the day, I had to sit on the couch with ice on my lips. "Why'd you do that, girl?

Why'd you put that iron on your lips?" My parents asked me. I was mad that they were still laughing at me. So, I just sat there.

"Why'd you do that, girl?

What made you do that?" They asked me again, as if they didn't hear me the first time. Finally, I removed the ice and screamed, "I wanted to see if the iron was hot!

So I...kissed it!" I don't think my parents had laughed that hard in a long time.

There was a lady that my momma was very good friends with. Her name was Sharon. She was a straight up hillbilly. She was also my godmother, and would give me anything.

It was probably about; let me see, two days after I kissed the iron. Sharon came over. My momma, explained to her what I had done, and that I could not eat. She told my momma, to put some Milk of Magnesia on my lips.

Within a couple of day all the skin on my lips still haven't completely healed. From that day on I left the ironing to my momma.

MEETING REAL MOMMA

The first time that I can remember meeting my real mother Grace, I was probably five years old. I was sitting in the house playing with my toys. Then there was a knock on the door.

My momma went to open the door. A short light-skinned woman was standing on the porch. She was wearing a wig. "Who there," my momma yelled? "It's me, momma.

"It's me, Grace!" My momma let her in.

I stopped playing with my toys, and began to stare at that woman. The woman was not ugly, and she looked like me. Linda, "This is your real momma. Baby, this is your momma Grace." My mouth hit the floor.

Now, I had always known that my momma was not my real momma. However, I had never met the woman. My momma explained that Grace had just gotten out of reform school. She was probably about, eighteen years old, and spent three years locked away.

To me, this woman was strange. I had never seen her before, yet I still felt an instant connection. I walked over to her and gave her a hug. I don't remember if she played with me or not, but I do remember her presence.

My real mother stayed around town for a couple of years. I heard about her through the grapevine, from different people. Blytheville, Arkansas was a small town, and all people did was gossip, gossip, gossip.

Mainly, they gossiped about my real mother. From what I am guessing, she had a very interesting life.

For about two years, after I first met my real mother, she stayed in Blytheville. I would hear from people around town that my real momma was pregnant. Umm, I was probably around seven years old then.

My real momma was staying with a friend at that time. Her name was Patty, and she was very nice to me. I can't remember how she looked, except that she was ugly. It wasn't that she was ugly. She just had a bad case of acne, and bad breath.

The next thing I know, my momma told me that my real momma had given birth to a baby. That same day, my momma took me to see my baby brother. I was so excited, because I had been the only child for years.

I wanted another sibling. When we got to Patty's house, they took me this bed that was in a dark room. My real momma showed all her teeth. When she said, "Linda, this is your baby brother Steven". I had to see him.

So, I climbed into the bed. There I saw this skinny, tiny baby, lying in the middle of the bed. He was all wrapped up in a white sheet. His skin was just so yellow. The hair on his head was blonde, and his eyes were blue.

I would say that he was only a couple months old then. "He too small!

No!

No!" My momma was yelling at me. Before I knew what happened. I was trying to pick him up.

"He too small.

Linda you'll drop him." My momma said in a softer voice. I never picked him up that day. The last thing I remembered. I stared at him, until it was time for us to leave. That was the last time that I ever saw my baby brother, Steven again.

Probably about a week or so later, we received the news that Steven had died. There was no funeral, or burial. At least not that I knew of. I do not even remember seeing my real mother around the time he died.

The rumor mill was working over time. I would hear that my real momma starved him to death. That was not true. Next thing I know. My momma told me that my real momma left Blytheville. She moved away to Fort Worth, Texas.

FIGHTING

When I started school all the kids used to pick on me. I guess the other kids were jealous or something. I don't know. All I do know is that I was teased a lot.

My momma used to buy me the cutest little dresses to go to school in. They were the ones with the slip already attached. The dresses were white, pink, and my favorite color red. I would have lace everywhere.

I couldn't help but to dress nice. My momma never shopped at the thrift stores. We would go through the JC Penny and Sears catalogs all the time. I would pick out what I wanted, and my momma ordered it.

Thrift stores were very popular for black people during that time in the South. The kids began teasing me about that. They would call me a little rich girl and always wanted to fight me.

There was this one girl, who picked on me all the time. She was ruthless. I do not know. Maybe I was also a target, because I didn't have any sisters or brothers. So I was like I had a target on my back

Her name was Ruthie Ann, but her name should have been ruthless. She stood above all the other girls in our grade. Her shoulders were huge, and they had muscles everywhere. She was a straight-up bully.

I would try to give her candy all the time. She would take my candy, and still want to fight me. I would try to give her my toys. Humph, nothing was ever enough to keep her from wanting to fight me.

My uncle John would pick me up from school. He would always drive this Black Buick. Whenever my parents were too busy, he would help out. Uncle John looked just like a black Santa Claus.

So as I walked out of school that day. I was completely minding my own business. Ruthless, I mean Ruthie ran up behind me. Then out of nowhere. She smacked me right in my eye, with her blue book bag. I was stunned, and immediately began to cry.

Uncle John came running up to me. He began patting my back saying, "Come on baby.

Come on with uncle.

It's going to be ok." He made me feel as if he understood.

Uncle John led me to his car, opened the door and gently placed me inside. I sat back in the passenger seat rubbing my eye. We got inside the house, and Uncle John said, "Baby go play". I didn't protest. I just ran off and grabbed my favorite doll.

He went inside the bedroom where my momma was. I could overhear them talking. Truthfully, I was not paying them any attention. I was busy combing my baby doll hair into a pony tail. My eye had stopped hurting by then.

I was just hoping to get a new toy. Normally when I was hurt, my parents would buy me a toy. So this time was no different. That was not until Uncle John called me into the bedroom. I went walking into the bedroom with fresh tears and my head to the floor.

When I walked in my eyes got big. Uncle John was waiting for me with his long brown belt in his hand. My uncle was a huge man. The belt looked like it could have wrapped around the earth with room to spare.

"Come here baby." I heard Uncle John say as he patted his leg. I looked to my momma and she just turned her head. "Come on over here to uncle." He kept patting his leg. I was confused.

"What?

What?

What did I do?" My fake tears now became real tears. I started to think of an excuse for what, I didn't know.

Uncle John had me lay on his lap face down. Every time I looked at him, he turned away. "Uncle John, wait!" I could barely catch my breath. "What did I do?" As soon as I finally lay across his big legs Uncle John wore my tail out.

I was so hurt. Uncle John had never whipped me before. When he was done, he stood me up, and held my hand. "Linda, listen to me now!

You need to fight back.

Do you hear me?

You need to fight back.

You hear me?" I stood there rubbing my butt, and nodding my head up and down.

I felt like I had sat in a fire pit. "Don't ever allow anyone to push you around like that!" Uncle John was looking me directly in my eyes now. He was hurt, because I was hurt.

It was then that I finally realized why he whipped me. Uncle John made it very clear, that every time I do not fight back. He was going to whip my butt himself. After my beating, I knew that I had to get Ruthie Ann back.

The next day I went to school on a mission. I knew what I had to do. There was no way that I was not going to succeed. My only mission was to get Ruthie Ann back.

I was so nervous sitting in class waiting for the end of day. Every time I looked at Ruthie Ann, I got pissed. I had just gotten my butt beat because of her. When school finally ended, I rushed outside the doors and spotted Uncle John waiting for me.

He was just standing outside his car. His huge arms were folded across his chest. I spotted Ruthie Ann walking out the doors. She was talking to her friends waving her arms in the air. Ruthie Ann never even looks my way.

She was acting as if she was a movie star. Waving and smiling at everyone. She began to walk down the three steps that were located right outside the building.

I was standing right behind the doors waiting on her exit.

As soon as she passed me, I made my move. I ran up behind her and smacked the dog shit out of her. Literally, I could have been an Olympic athlete or something. I bet she did not know what hit her until she saw my little white shoes hitting the pavement.

I ran straight to Uncle John. He was standing at his car looking shocked and proud all at once. His round cheeks were so puffy from smiling. I felt proud of myself!

I had gotten her good. Uncle John opened the car door and said, "Good job, baby"! I was walking on cloud nine for the entire ride home. Ruthie Ann, well, she never messed with me again since that incident.

Ha, I guess she learned her lesson. We would see each other in school, and she would go in the other direction. That was one of my greatest victories in my young years. I beat up a bully.

CHAPTER THREE

THE MEETING

I already told you, that my momma and daddy were church going people. The church that we attended was inside a small house with chairs lined up. Church's in the South were nothing like up North.

The churches were pretty much like a shack with a cross on the door. Most people attended the same church all the time. One Sunday in the summer of 1968, we went to church. Everything seemed normal, except there was a new member.

He was of average height for a man. His skin was brown, and he had huge arms. I cannot remember the service, but I can tell you that this man stood out. It was like he showed up from out of nowhere.

After the service was over, he introduced his self to us as Abihu Gray, a preacher. My daddy shook his hand and I could have sworn that he winked at me. Maybe I am just reaching for clues. I do not know. I just wished that meeting had never taken place.

My parents liked this preacher man. He would come by the house all the time. They would talk about the Bible and church matters. In the beginning, I thought that he was a good respectable preacher within our small town.

DADDY PASSING

On January 2, 1969, in the early morning hours my daddy passed away. It was the day after New Years.

Not even seven days after my birthday. I had just turned nine years old.

I was sitting in the living room playing with my toys. "Buddy, come here!" I heard my daddy call for my momma. "Buddy, come here, I wanna sit up!" He was calling her into the bedroom.

My daddy was already sick, and had been for a while. I'm not sure what caused his sickness. During that time, black people did not go to the doctor very often, especially in the Deep South.

The only time that black people went to the doctor's office. Was if they were severely ill. Pretty much, they would stay in pain until they died.

"Buddy, I want to look around." I heard him say. I was sitting on the floor playing with my toy train. My momma stopped cooking her greens and went to the bedroom. By me being so nosy, I went to the bedroom and stood in the doorway.

My momma was a very short woman, probably about four feet something. I watched her place her back to his. Then she leaned all of his weight onto her. Next, she pushed her feet up against the wall, and lifted my daddy, up into a sitting position.

I was in a daze looking at them. For some odd reason, my daddy looked right into my eyes. Then, right there, he took his last breath. I saw his chest rise, and fall. That was the last time that I saw my daddy alive.

As I looked out of the front window, and for a brief moment, everything turned dark. I saw nothing but darkness everywhere I turned. Then as if nothing ever happened it immediately turned to daylight again.

I didn't know what to do. It was as if momma knew that he was going to die. I ran in the bedroom with them. Where, momma and I started crying.

My momma called the funeral home to come and pick my daddy up. When, they took my daddy out of the house. It was the saddest day of my life.

His funeral was held at a Sanctified Church in Blytheville. There were mainly church people who came to pay their respects. The strange thing was that the preacher man actually gave the Eulogy over my daddy's casket. I can't remember anything he said though.

After the funeral, all the church people returned to our house to eat. Eating was not the only thing they did. They stole food, money, and everything they were able to get into their greedy hands. It was a shame how they just walked off with our stuff.

While my momma and myself were grieving, they were busy robbing us blind. After my daddy's funeral, we never saw those people again. They came in like the wind and left like thieves in the night.

MOVING IN

After the passing of my father, the preacher man began to come around a lot more frequently. My momma did not mind that at all. She was just eager to have a man in the house. She also liked him a lot.

We really did not know this man. The only thing that we knew about him was that he was a preacher. He was also taking care of his two young kids all by his self. The preacher man also had another son.

Later on we found out that he had another son. His name was Samuel. Samuel lived with his family in Chicago, but he was older than me.

He was a very likeable person in the beginning. The preacher man would come to the house to visit mama, and bring his two kids. I was so happy, because now I had someone to play with. Their names were Hezekiah and Azariah.

Azariah was five years old light skinned with short thick hair. Hezekiah was a one-year-old little boy with freckles. When they would come over, the preacher man would have me comb their hair, because he did not know what he was doing.

I treated his kids like my little dolls. I would dress them up, and comb Azariah's hair all the time. I loved when they came around. Since I was the only child, I welcomed the company.

The strange thing was that we never saw their mothers. They had separate mommas, which during that time especially in the South was strange. Neither Hezekiah's mom nor Azariah's mom came around a lot.

The preacher man was living in terrible living conditions. One day momma, and myself went with the preacher man's to his house. He needed to some clean clothes for Hezekiah and Azariah. When, we got to his house. I would have sworn that no one lived there.

It was a raggedy shack. There was no furniture inside except for a dirty mattress on the floor. Dirty clothes were everywhere. The house smelled horrible. Literally, I felt bad for them.

There were all types of animals running around everywhere. It was like an indoor farm. I almost ran out when I saw a pig walking around in the kitchen. A goat was looking through the back window. His house was a wreck.

We had to search through the dirty clothes. Just to find something for Hezekiah and Azariah to wear. The rest of the clothes were ruined with urine, and animal poop. So we just threw them away.

The preacher man was nice to me, but he was sweeter on my momma. He treated me as if I was his child then. Everything was normal. Our house had turned into a home again.

The preacher man even told me to call him daddy. Matter of fact, he later demanded that I called him daddy. Even when he was raping me, I had to call him daddy.

I cannot remember the exact day that he began to touch me. However, I do remember that he was about thirty-three years old. My age, um, I was nine years old.

At that time I was developed more that the average young girl. I had breasts and hips. My shape looked like a teenager. All I would ever wear was stretch pants, and long tee-shirts. The stretch pants were an odd multi-colored.

The preacher man started coming around a lot. He was always wearing something dark. I thought that he only had two pair of slacks. They were brown or a dark gray. Maybe they could have been dingy black.

I would notice how he allowed his daughter Azariah to sit next to him on the couch. We had this ugly brown blanket. The preacher man would sit with it across their legs.

I began to sit on the other side of him. My chest had become his little play ground. We had one couch and a chair that my momma would sit in. His son would be sitting on the floor. Everyone's eyes would be glued to the TV.

I was so young and ignorant at the time. It was just all weird. I didn't know what he was doing was wrong. Everything was a joke. I would laugh and giggle when the preacher man was touching me. Nothing seemed strange to me at first.

Whenever, my momma was not around, or not paying attention, he would touch me. I would tell Azariah about it, and we both would laugh. Since we were so young, nothing seemed wrong then.

Azariah was like my younger sister. I would tell her everything. Even though she was only five years old, humph, that was my confidant. Azariah was like my little best friend.

My parents raised me to respect preachers, not fear them. Besides that he didn't start off mean. It was like the preacher man was an actor in the beginning. He courted my momma for about a couple of months. She allowed him to come in and take my daddy's place.

The preacher man took over our money, our house, and us. It was not until the fall of 1969, that he and his kids moved in. I went from being an only child, to one of three. Almost one year after my daddy died, my world was turned upside down.

The preacher man went to my momma, and told her that his roof was leaking. He and his kids were going to be homeless. My momma was just so eager to have a man in the house. So she eagerly agreed to let them move in.

FIRST NIGHT

The very first day that the preacher man and his kids moved in, everything changed. I almost lost my virginity at ten-years old. My childhood days, officially ended.

Since my daddy had passed. My sleeping arraignments never changed. I still slept in my momma's bedroom. The preacher man's kids slept on the couch, in the living room.

This was the fall of 1971. Everyone had settled in for the night. Hezekiah and Azariah were already sleeping. "Why?"

Why, Preacher man?" I overheard my momma ask the preacher man. I was lying in my bed supposed to be sleep. His voice was very deep. So it was hard for him to talk low.

"I have to sleep in Linda's bed.

If I don't she's gonna tell those people on me." I didn't know what he meant by that. My momma was quiet for a brief minute. "What?

What do you mean preacher man? What people?" He paused, "them Government people!" His voice was getting louder.

"Those Social Security and Veteran's people!

She gonna tell them about me!" I caught a lump in my throat. "Preacher man, she not gonna tell no one." I finally heard my momma speak.

"Look!

I'm done talking!" That was it. End of conversation. Case closed. There was no arguing with him. So she just gave in.

Truly, I didn't understand what he meant about me telling. First off, I would not know whom to tell. Secondly, I didn't care. Thirdly, I didn't even know what

I was not supposed to tell. I was just a child, and wanted to stay one.

By this time, my momma was in her seventies, and all she wanted, was a man in the house. Her eyesight was getting worse. The house constantly needed some work done. Everything was falling apart.

That very first night, the preacher man crawled in bed with me. I was still facing the wall. For a minute, nothing happened. I began to come out of the fetal position. My eyes finally gave into the sandman.

I woke up to my momma snoring and his hands were all over me. He slid his hands under my pink nightgown. Then he pulled my little white panties off. As I attempted to pull away, he held me tighter.

I was shocked, and scared. I didn't know what to do. He made me lay on my back. Then he got on top of me. It felt like he was crushing my wind pipe. My young body was stuck under him.

I could not breathe. There was a marching band going on in my chest. I could not scream. Even though, he had never whipped me before. I knew that if I woke my momma up. I would have gotten beat.

He had such, a mean look on his face. Without him saying anything, I knew that this was going to be my secret to keep. My breathing was getting louder. "Shut up! Those were the only words that the preacher man said to me.

I tried to push away the pain, and just lay there. I silently cried, as he attempted to penetrate me. It was so painful. Oh God, I thought that I was going to die. He continued to try, until he got tired.

Since, I was only ten years old and a virgin. He could not get inside me that night. The preacher man just rolled off me. Pushed me aside like a rag doll, and got out of bed.

I thought that my eyes were playing tricks on me. He climbed into bed with my momma right after that. I had to listen to him have sex with her.

"Please let him stay there!

Please let him stay there!

Please let him stay there!" I prayed and prayed that he continued to have sex with my momma.

Then, he would not need me. Unfortunately, the next night, he tried again but, it still did not work. The preacher man tried for a whole week to penetrate me, until finally he succeeded.

Ooh Lord the pain was so intense. I wanted to die. My entire world turned black that night. I woke up the next day to bloody panties and a bedspread. I knew then, that I was no longer a child.

REAL MOMMA RETURNS

The next time that I heard from my real mother, I was ten years old. She wrote me a letter. She had always known my address. Therefore, finding me was never an issue for her.

My real momma would write me letters asking about how my momma and daddy were doing. She wanted to know how I was doing in school, or just to tell me when she was coming to visit.

Writing letters was her way of checking on me. She would send me wigs, since my hair was so thin. I would always wear my hair in a pony on the top of my head. I figure that was her way of taking care of me from afar.

I would tell my real momma everything in the letters. Pretty much, that was how we communicated whenever she left town. Therefore, when my daddy died and my momma moved the preacher in. I told my real momma.

I wrote her and said, "Hi ma, daddy passed away.

Momma got a new man, and he's messing with me.

Can you please come and get me?" My real momma wrote me back saying, "I'll be in Blytheville soon"! That was her only response.

The preacher man found my letter, because I was young and careless with hiding them. Not soon after he read the letter. Word got around that, my real mother was in town. When she returned, she had moved in with her, "special female friend".

There were rumors about my real momma and that woman having a special relationship. I was too young to care. I can't remember her name, but I do remember her being tall. She was always nice to me.

Anyway, the preacher man packed us into his Blue Chevrolet pick-up. Then we headed for my real momma's friend house. So that he could confront her.

We all entered this house that looked ugly on the outside. Once we got inside it was so neat and clean. All the furniture matched. My momma and I went to sit on the couch with the, "special friend". The both of them were sitting at a round table playing with the cards.

My real momma was wearing a pretty purple shirt. It was all silky and shiny. She had on a curly wig and it hung on her shoulders. Her little eyes were glued to us as we entered the front door.

The preacher man and my real momma immediately began to argue. My real momma was questioning the preacher man about what he was doing to me. They were arguing so tuff. I thought that he was going to hit her. She was no joke.

My real momma was not backing down until he told her, "If you want your daughter back!

You have to pay momma Strong back for everyday that she had to feed and clothe Linda!

Beginning from when she was two years old!" She just gave in.

The preacher man walk out of that house with me to do whatever he pleased. My real momma was only in her twenties. She didn't know what to do. That was the last time that my real momma attempted to get me back.

On the ride home, I was hurt, mad, and scared. I knew that he was going to whip me once we got home. Just by the way I heard him sucking his teeth. Sucking his teeth was something he did we he was mad.

As soon as we got home, he began whipping me. This was not the usual whipping with a belt. It was a beating. He slapped me to the point where I thought my neck was broken.

It didn't matter what he got his hands on, he used it on me. There was even a huge stick that I thought he broke over my back. I was beat that day as if I was his woman, and I was only ten years old.

From that day on, I never stopped writing my real momma. I just got a lot smarter about where I hid the letters. The preacher man would watch the mail. Then he would beat me, if he found anything from my real momma. So I got very clever with hiding them.

I started to hide them in the couch. Sometimes I would put them in between my bed mattress. I had to do all that I could to stay in contact with my real momma. She was the only person, who I was able to tell about the nasty things that he did to me.

My real momma could not stand the preacher man. She stopped coming around after the last incident. I did not see my real mother again, until I was fourteen years old.

CHAPTER FOUR

THE DAY I TOLD

I was in either the fifth or the sixth grade at this time. My age, was probably twelve years old, and my teachers were Ms. Greene and Mrs. Morris. I liked both my teacher's, because I had been in their classes since the fourth grade.

Miss Green was a tall skinny black woman that was nice. Mrs. Morris, was a light-skinned tall, fat woman whose, husband was a cop. They were both good teachers that really looked out for their students.

One day during Miss Green class, she pulled me out in the hallway to talk to me. When I walked into the hall I saw Mrs. Morris out there too. Miss Green, came right out and asked me, "Linda, why is your hygiene different"? I began to look down at my dirty shoes.

Back then, we did not shower regularly. Once the preacher man moved in everything stopped. I knew that I smelled. I started having a period. It was hard to stay clean, because the preacher man would just dirty me back up.

"Linda, is anything going on?

You could talk to us.

Is anyone hurting you?" They both were grilling me with multiple questions.

"Linda honey, you smell." The both of them kept talking nonstop.

"No!"

Nothing is going on!

No one is messing with me!" My eyes were now looking at Mrs. Morris black heels. I knew that I could not tell regardless of what they said.

"Linda, you could tell us.

It's ok tell us if someone messing with you." I started breathing heavy. Once I looked at my dirty white shoes again. I noticed a couple of wet drops. It wasn't until I realized that the wet spots were my tears. My shoulders dropped.

"My momma got a new man!

He had been touching me!" So right there, in the hallway, I blurted it out. I told the house secret. It became very hard for me to catch my breath. There were sounds coming from my body that scared me.

"It's ok.

Linda, it's ok.

It's ok." They were trying their best to console me. I eventually got myself together after a few minutes of their hugs. Walking back into class was like walking onto a firing range.

All the other kids were just looking at me as if I had gotten into trouble. I went back to my seat, which was in the first row. My head felt heavy as it hit my desk. I was feeling so embarrassed.

There were all sorts of thoughts going to my head. When, everyone began whispering, pointing, and laughing at me. I pretended not to hear them. It was pretty much the end of the day.

Next thing I know, Miss Green entered the class and her eyes were just as puff as mine. She just dismissed everyone for the day. I got up out of my seat, and was the first one out the door. I went home, not realizing what I had actually done.

About an hour after I got home. I looked out the front window, and saw a red car pull up in front of the house. Once I got a better look inside the car. I realized that both Miss Green and Mrs. Morris were inside the car.

My heart stopped immediately, because I knew why they were here. I ran away from the window, and went to where Hezekiah and Azariah were. The horn began blaring, and my momma went outside to talk to them.

Once, my momma was outside, they asked her where her new man was. My momma called the preacher man outside. I watched from the window, as they stood on the gravel road talking.

I could not make out everything that they were saying. “Naw, that ain’t going on here!”

Ain’t nothing like that going on here!” I was able to hear my momma say. I knew they asked my momma, did she know that her new man was touching me. As they were talking, the preacher man, turned his head to the side, and began sucking his teeth.

Sucking his teeth was something that he would do, when he was mad. The preacher man was only five feet five, and a very scary looking man. He had one of the most intimidating looks in his eyes. It was one that I had never seen before.

"If you are touching Linda!

You are going to go to prison!" Mrs. Morris finger was flapping in the air as she shouted that to the preacher man. She said a couple of other choice words, which I could not make out.

They knew that he was lying. He may have fooled everyone else, but not them. Both Miss Green and Mrs. Morris, got in their car, and drove away. I ran from the window, and went back over to where, Hezekiah and Azariah were playing.

Hezekiah was two years old, and Azariah was six years old then. They were clueless to what was happening. I just sat there, and waited for them to come inside.

"Linda!

Linda, where you at girl?

Come here?" I heard the preacher man yelling. I was shaking in the corner of the wall. "Linda, get over her now!" I pried my feet from the floor and walked over to him.

"Why did you tell your teachers that lie?

Why, are you trying to ruin your momma's life?" He grabbed my arms and began shaking me. I began to cry and said, "Naw, I ain't say nothing like that!

I didn't say nothing to them! My momma was sitting on the couch looking at me. I turned to her and said, "Momma I'm sorry!

I didn't mean it!" I was having a hard time reading her face.

By that time, the preacher man had convinced my momma, that I was lying. Then by telling those lies, she could be cut off SSI, and lose my father's pension. My momma was so afraid of losing her financial support. She immediately believed the preacher man.

As a result, both my parents whipped me. I was beat so bad that day. My butt was probably a different color. I honestly thought that he was going to kill me.

My body was so bruised and sore that day. I never again, told anyone about the abuse, except for my real momma. From that point on, whatever happened in our household, stayed in the household.

MOVE TO AMARELLE

Immediately after that incident, the preacher man had my momma take me out of school. I never saw Miss Green or Mrs. Morris anymore after that day. The last memory that I have of them, was when they left my house driving down the gravel road.

The preacher man must have gotten paranoid, or something. He was worried, that my teachers were going to tell the law on him. Within a month, he had convinced my momma, to take her money out of the bank.

Then, he gave Azariah back to her mother. He was going to give Hezekiah back to his mother, but changed his mind. Azariah needed to be enrolled into school, but Hezekiah was too young then. For whatever reason, Hezekiah remained with the preacher man.

Within a week, the preacher man convinced my momma to sell the house that my daddy built. They also sold all of the land. He moved all of us to a small city, in Arkansas called Amarelle.

He bought five and a half acres for five hundred dollars. The preacher man built two houses on that land. Both house had a tin roof on them. One was a three-bedroom shack with dirt floors.

The first house only had a bedroom, living room, and a homemade kitchen. There was no indoor plumbing. We had to use an outhouse for the bathroom. There was no indoor shower or a bathtub.

The second house was also a three-bedroom shack. It had three rooms, which was a bedroom that I slept in. Then the preacher man turned the living room into my momma's room.

This was weird because my bedroom was his primary room. He would go in my momma's room and have sex with her. Then the preacher man would come into my room and rape me.

The first house, the preacher man built a fireplace in the make shift kitchen. Even though we lived in Arkansas, it still would get cold. I would use it as a stove to cook on. A lot of the meat that I cooked was rotten meat.

Our house always smelled of rotten chicken. I would have to soak it in baking soda for hours. We used to have a huge pale that I had to carry that was full of chicken. My favorite thing was to fry the chicken.

We would eat anything back then. Half the time when we were not buying rotten meat from the grocery store. We killed our own food right there in the back yard.

We had all types of animals. There was a hog, a goat, a cow, and chickens. Twice a year we slaughtered those animals, so that we could eat. Hey, at least it was fresh meat. We were eating pork chops ham and steak. My favorite was the hog meat.

He moved us smack dab in the middle of the country. The refrigerator sat on the front porch. All aspects of modern life were gone. The preacher man was crazy. I often wondered why my momma agreed to this man's craziness but hey, she was old.

Personally, I think that after my dad died, she just gave up. He took advantage of my momma. He made her feel like she could do nothing without him. The preacher man scared her also. He would beat on her a lot.

If she did not give him money, he would beat her. There were times where my momma would stick up for me, and he would beat her. She took a lot of beatings from him. He would even beat her is she did not call him preacher. She probably took just as many knocks upside the head as I did.

MY NEW LIFE

The preacher man was very jealous. I could not talk to anyone, male or female. If someone talked to me, he would beat me. I could not look at anyone and if someone looked at me, I got beat. My entire life had to revolve around the preacher man.

Literally, every night I had to kiss the preacher man's private. I had to do so many nasty and dirty things. I could not protest, because he would beat me. There was nothing, which he did not have me do.

He would tell me about the spells he placed on people. That man actually believed that he could make people do anything that he wanted them to do. The preacher man would carry around two books all the time.

One was the Holy Bible and the other one was a black book that consisted of hoodoo voodoo. He believed in witchcraft, and the black book consisted of spells. He actually thought that he could put spells on people. The sad fact is that I actually believed him.

He told me one day, that when we purchased the land in Amarelle. We only got it because he put a spell on the white guy. The preacher man was talking about the white guy who owned the pawnshop back in Blytheville.

He thought that as long as he had his hand on the voodoo book people would do as he pleased. His prayers were not any prayers; however, they were prayers out of the black voodoo book. He would say those prayers to momma and me when we did not do what he told us to do.

I actually cannot recall a time when he was not carrying that black book or the Bible. The preacher man knew the Bible backwards and forwards. He knew all sixty-six books in the Bible. He even made us read the Bible everyday faithfully. I would read the Bible so much to where I know most of the stories by heart.

The preacher man would read Psalms all the time. His favorite was the book of Psalms. Psalms ninety-one was his favorite. He would read this particular Psalm religiously. The ironic thing is that Psalm 91 is a prayer for protection.

Law enforcement officers, soldiers, firefighters, mainly people who needed protection under intense life or death situations would recite Psalms 91 daily. Maybe I should have been reciting it myself.

He was not a preacher in my eyes. He was a child molester. He was a woman abuser. The preacher man was a crazy psycho who stole my childhood, adolescent, and adult hood. If I do not tell my story, I will probably go crazy myself.

He had me believing in his ability to put spells on people. I was just a child. He actually told me one day that it did not matter who I told, because no one would believe me. He said that he had everyone under a spell.

I had no other choice but to believe him, since no one believed me anyway. Everyone thought that I was a fast little girl. Honestly, I had no one to tell anyway. People talked so much crap about me back then. It still hurts to this day.

They used to say that I stole my momma's boyfriend. How could I steal my momma's thirty-three year old boyfriend? Hell, I did not want him. She could have gladly came and got him out of my bed every night.

All I wanted to do was be a child. I wanted to go to school and attend school activities. I wanted to hang out with my friends. Get my own boyfriend that was my own age. I wanted to do the things that I saw each of my friends' doing.

I would have never chosen to have sex with the preacher man. People amazed me back then. No one ever looked at the reality of the situation. He was a grown man having sex with a twelve-year-old girl, and that is wrong.

Therefore, as a child I believed him when he would say that he had everyone under his spell. My own momma couldn't even help me. The teachers could not help me. My real momma was unsuccessful. I was just stuck.

When we moved to Amarelle, he did allow me to start back going to school. He was afraid of me telling anyone else what he was doing to me. In all honesty, he had nothing to worry about. He had me trained and terrified.

I knew that if I told anyone they, would not believe me. Then once the preacher man got a hold of me, he would beat the life out of me for telling. Pretty much, I was not telling.

School was a safe haven for me during that time. Going to school, was an escape from the physical and sexual abuse, I had to endure. I would lose myself and forget about all my troubles while I was in class.

I attended school for probably about a couple of months. Then I started crushing on this boy named John Henry. He was so cute and popular. This was the first guy to really pay me any type of attention.

John Henry was very tall. He was dark and skinny, with curly jet-black hair. He played basketball for Amarelle High. Which surprised me, to find out he liked me too. Considering, the fact that I was not one of the pretty girls in school.

One day, he wanted me to go to the school's basketball game with him. I really wanted to go, but I knew that the preacher man would not allow it. John Henry insisted on coming to my house to ask the preacher man could I go to the game.

I told him not to come over. I knew that he would beat me. John Henry and I talked a lot. I would tell him some things about the preacher man, but I guess he did not believe me.

Therefore, on the day of the game all hell broke loose. John Henry did not listen to me. He came over my house anyway to ask the preacher man if I could go to the game.

That same day I left school and went home. I was in the house doing my unlimited list of chores, when I heard a knock at the door. I looked outside and saw John Henry standing out there. I almost shit my pants.

I ran to the door and asked him, "Why did you come here"? He stood there looking at me as if I was over reacting. I whispered again so the preacher man would not here me, "Why did you come here?

I told you that I'm going to get into trouble!" My mind began racing a mile a minute, because I knew this was going to be bad. Before he had a chance to respond, the preacher appeared at the door.

John Henry asked him could I go to the basket ball game. The preacher man said, "No!" He then waved his hand at John Henry, and told me to go inside the house.

So, when the preacher man entered the house. He started sucking his teeth. Then he gave me that look. I knew that I was going to die.

He beat me so bad that day. He never allowed me to go back to school. I never saw John Henry again after that. I was then completely isolated from everyone except my momma, and my real momma whenever she came around.

He was not afraid of anyone telling, because he beat my momma too. Strange thing was that he never beat my real mother. He would just threaten her a lot.

He always would tell her that he will call the cops on her. The preacher man's main threat was that he would tell police that she abandoned her child. Then, he would say that she would have to pay them back for raising me.

My real momma was young. She just did not know how to get me out of that situation. The preacher man had total control over everything that I did. I could not talk to anyone if he was not around. I walked around like a zombie most of the time.

My Bible became my best friend. At some point, all I was doing was, existing. My life as Linda K. Strong officially ended. I was now the property of the preacher man.

CHAPTER FIVE

FIRST PREGNANCY

Almost exactly two years after the preacher began raping me. I got pregnant. I was thirteen years old. I noticed that I stopped having my period. When I was in school, I learned that if a girl skips a period that meant she was pregnant.

I was so scared. I didn't know what to do, or who to tell. I knew that he was going to beat me. Even though I knew that it was his fault, somehow the preacher man was going to make it my fault that I got pregnant.

Therefore, I began wearing tight clothes to hide my growing belly. Sometimes I would wear layers and layers of clothes, but nothing ever worked. I could not go anywhere and no one ever visited us.

Then one day, my momma and the preacher man found out. I do not exactly know how, but they did. Well they had no other choice, because I had began to get big. My stomach was becoming too big to hide anymore.

They called me in the house and sat a chair in the middle of the living room floor. As I sat in the chair looking at the both of them stare at me. "Tell me who the father is, girl!" My momma started by yelling.

I began to panic. I knew that I could not tell my momma that the preacher man was the father so I began to cry. I looked up at her and she yelled again, "Tell me who the father is!"

You better tell me who you been sleeping with!" I could feel the preacher man's hot breath on my neck.

Who you been sleeping with?" With every word that came out of her mouth, I felt the spit on the side of my face.

On my other side I heard the preacher man sucking his teeth. I was afraid to look his way. Then out of nowhere, my momma slapped me so hard. I felt her hand print on the other side of my face.

She was still screaming, "Who you been sleeping with?

Tell me who is it!" I still refused to talk. Then all of sudden she began hitting me non-stop screaming, "Tell me!

Tell me!" Out of nowhere the other side of my face started to burn.

It was the preacher man. Now, he was on the other side of me slapping me and knocking me upside my head. He was screaming, "Yeah tell us!

Tell us who you slept with, girl!" My head felt like a punching bag.

In reality, he did not want me to tell. He was beating me so that I would not tell he was the father. The preacher man just did not want my momma to know. My face was burning.

"Donald Brown!

It's Donald Brown's baby!

I slept with him!

I'm sorry!

I'm so sorry."

As soon as I screamed Donald Brown was the father.

They stopped beating me. All I felt were eyes burning through the back of my head. I had never had sex with that person, but I knew that he was a good boy from my class.

I met him in the short months that I attended Amarelle High. I knew that I would never see him again. Therefore, I just blurted his name out, "Donald Brown"! I only said his name because it was the first name that came to mind.

The preacher man then walked away without saying a word. My momma just stood there looking at me, with her mouth open. Honestly, I believe that she knew I was lying. She never said another word.

She just walked away. That was it. Words cannot describe my emotional state. I was so pissed and hurt that I didn't know what to do.

Here I am young, abused and pregnant with no one to turn to. I felt lost. All I could think to do was getting rid of it. I did not want a baby.

I ran outside and sat on the front porch. My mind was running with a lot of different ways to end my unborn child's life. The only idea that I came up with was to jump off the front porch.

I was hugely pregnant and badly beaten. I had no friend's, no family. I was still a child and knew nothing about raising kids. I was scared, and the only solution that came to mind was to kill the baby.

As, I stood on the front porch looking for ways to kill the baby nothing stood out. Then all of a sudden, I looked down and it hit me. I decided to jump off the porch. I wanted to land on my belly. Hopefully, I would have a miscarriage.

The front porch was only about a foot or foot and half high. I stood up, closed my eyes, took a deep breath, and jumped. When I opened my eyes, I was standing on both feet with my big belly poking out.

I looked around realizing that it did not work and screamed, "Dammit"! I was pissed off. Then again, I was only fifteen years old. My mind was all over the place. Hey, it was wishful thinking on my part.

Once I realized I was still pregnant. I sat back down on the front porch and prayed. "Please God.

Please God, give me strength." The more I carried my baby, the more that I began to love her.

IN LABOR

I didn't know anything about having a baby. No one told me anything either. I was very confused. Actually, my momma and the preacher man treated me worse since they found out that I was pregnant.

There were no doctor appointments, pregnancy classes, baby shower, or congratulations. The people in our small town would tease me. I was so embarrassed. They called me the fast girl that got her self pregnant at the age of thirteen.

On April 5, 1973 in the morning, I began to feel constipated. My stomach began to hurt so badly. I thought that I had a bad case of gas. It never occurred to me that I was in labor.

I was now fourteen years old, and in terrible pain. I was all alone in the house. I went to lie on my bed to try to ease the pain, but that did not work. I began rolling all over the bed, until I felt that I had to shit.

We had to use buckets when we went the bathroom. There was already a bucket in our bedroom. Therefore, I sat on the bucket thinking that I was about to do number two.

I began to push, and push, and push. Then a head popped out. I got scared and jumped back in bed.

I still had to push so I continued to push until the baby popped out.

I was terrified, because I knew that the preacher man was going to beat me. Once he found out that I had the baby. The only thing that I could think of was to try to push the baby back up in me. Of course that did not work.

Next, I placed a cover over the baby. Then, I pulled the cover all the way up to my neck. All of a sudden, the baby started to cry. I was so surprised to hear something that came from me, cry.

My momma and the preacher man rushed into the bedroom. The preacher man snatched the cover off me and saw the baby. I could tell that he was pissed.

He told me to wrap the baby up, and put the after birth in a bag.

I did exactly what he told me to do. He rushed all of us into his pick-up so that we can go to the hospital. I was in so much pain, that I do not even remember the drive there.

We drove to the clinic in Osceola, Arkansas, a town outside of Amarelle. There was no clinic in our small town, so we had to drive that far. It was also the only hospital in Osceola, to treat black people.

They cut the after birth, washed my baby up, and placed a white cloth diaper on it. It was so adorable and I could not stop staring at the baby. Then the doctor handed me my four-pound baby girl.

I named my baby Bathsheba Ann Brown. I just thought of her name off the top of my head. Maybe the name came to me, because Bathsheba is the preacher man's mother name. I then gave her the middle name of Ann, and the last name of Brown.

That was no one will know that she was the preacher man's baby. Even though, I hated the preacher man, I was glad to have my baby-girl. Bathsheba became my reason to keep living.

She was born premature. We did not have any money to pay for the incubator, so the doctors told me to take my baby home that same day. I was so scared, but the doctors didn't care.

FIRST VISIT TO DETROIT

I would also call our backyard a mini farm. Where I had to chop cotton, milk cows, and heard the chickens. I actually, had to cut off their heads so that we could eat dinner. I was responsible for slopping the hog's. They would eat out of a five-gallon pale, which I had to carry.

It was terrible, especially, when I had to clean up the poop from the horses, the dogs, the pigs, the rooster, the hens, and cats. I learned that pregnancy was not a beautiful thing.

My skin was dark. I kept my hair in one ponytail that was on the top of my head. My teeth still looked like dogs teeth. All my clothes came from a mission, or they were given to me.

I had gained some weight from my pregnancy, which never left. Personally, I would not call myself large, but I did get a little chunky. However, I looked sickly, due to all the stress that I was under.

From what we knew about the preacher man, he had very little family in Arkansas. He would always brag about his uncle that lived in Detroit. He told me that his uncle was a bishop, who had a big church in Detroit.

The preacher man looked up to his uncle Robert. He would brag about how Detroit, was such a nice place to live. He loved his family up North, and wanted them to meet his kids.

One day, the preacher man decided that we would all go visit his uncle in Detroit. I think it was right after I had Bathsheba in 1973. We took our first trip to Detroit.

I was ecstatic, because I had never been outside of Arkansas. To be perfectly honest, I don't remember too much of that trip, because I had just had Bathsheba, who was only three months old.

I literally walked around in a daze. We arrived in Detroit after a long ten-hour drive. His uncle Robert allowed us to stay with his family. My first impression of Uncle Robert was that I liked him.

He was a short chubby man, with a huge smile. He and his wife struck me as people that I can trust. Uncle Robert's wife was a little older than me. Her name was Shiloh.

I liked her a lot. She was skinny, and very pretty. Shiloh had a very pretty voice. One thing about her was that she was always cooking. She and I hit it off very quick.

For some strange reason, I began to tell Shiloh about what was going on. I told her about how the preacher man was raping me, and that Bathsheba was his daughter. She was shocked, and immediately told Uncle Robert.

When I finally told Shiloh, I didn't know if they were going to help me. It just felt good to get if off my chest. She was the first person that actually listened to me.

The first visit to Detroit did not last that long. I could not go anywhere without the preacher man. The one good thing about that trip was that I met my first friend, Shiloh. She and I exchanged phone numbers when we left.

EZEKIEL

When I discovered that I was pregnant again. I was around three or four months. I didn't have to hide this pregnancy. Truthfully, I do not remember too much about my pregnancy. Not until the time I gave, birth.

It was September of 1974, when I gave birth to my baby boy. I had him in the same Osceola clinic where I had my first baby. I remember looking at my baby boy, and noticing that he looked very different.

He was not that small. He was six pounds something ounces. The preacher man named him Ezekiel Strong. My momma gave him her last name. That was weird, since, we never discussed who the father was this time.

Ezekiel was born with light skin, or it was like red or something. He had a head full of this reddish brown hair. His eyes were also very light brown, and almost somewhat unreal.

The preacher man got him a baby bed from a mission. The crib was right by my bed so that I can get to him when he cried. Bathsheba would sleep with my momma in her room. My momma would cook greens for her and Bathsheba to eat a lot.

The preacher man would sleep with my momma in her room. Then he would come into my bed with me and my baby. That bedroom had become very crowded.

I would get up every morning and feed my baby. Every time he cried, I would get up with no problem and place a bottle in his mouth. Just like that, he would be out like a rock.

One morning, I woke up, and my baby was not crying. When I went to pick him up, he was as stiff as a board. I was so scared. There was no one in the room with me. Everyone else was sitting by the fireplace trying to keep warm.

It is weird, but I can't remember too much that happened after that. Maybe it was because I don't want to remember. I didn't know what to do. Emotionally, I felt nothing.

Next thing, that I can recall, was when we all arrived at the hospital. "Your baby is dead." I had to look up just to see who was talking. It was the preacher man and he was walking away from a white doctor. I was like, "Ok."

Ezekiel had only lived one month and some weeks. Then just like that. He was dead. Truthfully speaking, I felt nothing. I had zero emotions.

I am so frustrated with myself! It annoys me, when I cannot remember the day of my baby's birth or death. I guess after all of the beatings that the preacher man had given me, left nothing in my brain.

I had taken so many licks up side my head. To the point to where I was completely dead up there. I had no emotions or thoughts of my own. It was just another day to me.

Once we left the hospital. We went to the same funeral home. Not any funeral home, but the same one that we dug graves for. We walked in carrying Ezekiel in a little box. The preacher man then arranged for his burial.

There was no funeral or mourning sympathetic faces. No one offered me condolences or a prayer of comfort. It was only my momma, Bathsheba, the preacher man, his son, and me. All of this was happening in the same day Ezekiel died.

Once we got to the cemetery. I looked up and saw clouds all over the sky. The wind was beating my face. My back felt like someone was pushing me from behind, but no one was there.

We headed out into the dirt. The preacher man picked up this black shovel. He shoved it at me and said, "You're going to dig his grave"! I was standing there holding Bathsheba's hand.

"I don't know what you standing there looking all stupid for!" Bathsheba let go of my hand and I just took the shovel. "And hurry up! I ain't got all day!" So that's what I did. I dug my son's grave.

I didn't protest, or blink an eye. Immediately, I began to dig my son's grave. I dug that grave until it was deep enough. I took the box. I placed my baby boy in that hole. I threw the dirt over his grave and the coffin.

If I can recall, I do remember the preacher man saying, a small eulogy over his body. Truthfully, I do not know what he said. Actually, I don't think that Ezekiel's death even registered in my mind.

I never cried, or shed a tear. All I remember was, walking away, and never seeing my baby again. It was weird, because no one ever talked about how or why my baby died.

The preacher man did tell me that, he believed the spirits killed Ezekiel. He believed that because, he said that he was digging for their treasure. The spirits were punishing him for getting close to the hidden treasure.

Sounds crazy, but it is true. He literally thought that the spirits were after him. He actually dug up the floors in the house and the backyard looking for treasure. The preacher man would tell us that there was buried treasure in the house.

He believed in spirits, and thought that the spirits had buried treasure under our house. He thought that the voodoo book he carried, kept the spirits away. Our living room, no longer had a floor. It now consisted of large holes everywhere.

He had us digging up the entire house looking for treasure. We were like on a scavenger hunt all the time. The backyard consisted of nothing but holes everywhere. It was like a scene out of a horror movie. The backyard and the living room were like a construction zone.

At least once a day, the preacher man thought that he had found some gold. He would find little things like a broken watch, or something little. However, he never found anything that was worth something.

CHAPTER SIX

MORE PREGNANCIES

I pretty much became a baby-making machine after that. I would say a couple of months or so later. I was pregnant again. By this time, I knew that I was pregnant, but I didn't know how many months.

It was definitely in the beginning, because I was not showing. My momma, well she had tuned out by that time. It was pretty much, like another day in my life.

It all started on a hot June day in 1975. I had been working in the field all day. So I was carrying that big five gallon pale, full of slop for the hogs. Then all of a sudden, I began to feel a lot of pain in my stomach.

I knew immediately that something was wrong. There was no one that I could tell, so I said nothing. It was very evident, that no one was going to help me. The preacher man probably would have beaten me for saying that my stomach hurt, anyway.

The preacher man had a lot of odd jobs. Cutting grass and digging graves, were just a couple of them. It seemed as if, we never had any money. He would keep a very tight leash on all of us. The preacher man was just paranoid that someone would find out the truth.

We all piled into his Blue Ford pick-up. He had to go and cut someone's grass. All of us piled into that big front seat. It was very hot that day but, not unusual for Amarelle.

When we got to where he was going to cut grass. He and his son got out the truck, and left me, momma, and Bathsheba inside. My stomach felt like the inside was going to burst open. I just sat there without saying a word.

Then, I began to feel all sticky down there. My stomach was hurting so bad. I didn't know what to do.

My back was throbbing, and I couldn't get comfortable. I just continued to sit there, as if nothing was wrong.

Everything began to feel all warm down there. I didn't know if it was sweat. I thought that I had pissed on myself. All I knew was that I felt nasty!

I put my hand down there hoping that it was only sweat. Then when I pulled my hand up, it was all thick and squishy. My stomach flipped when I realized what I had. I picked up the after birth in the palm of my hand.

I continued to sit in the seat without saying anything. Momma, Bathsheba, and I sat in that pick-up for a couple more minutes, before the preacher man returned. I never said anything, and he just pulled off.

We got back home and everyone got out the truck, including me. There was blood all in the seat, and on me. I know that I smelled worst than I normally did. My clothes were soiled with blood. I was a hot mess when we got out of the car.

Once I got in the house, I went to wipe myself off, and change clothes. Then I went on about my day as usual. My momma said nothing at all. She was old, and pretty much lost her eyesight as well as all of her fight.

PRAYER

In the month of September, in the same year, just three months after my miscarriage. I was pregnant again. Now, let me see, this will make baby number four for me. I had absolutely no control over my life.

For whatever reason, I had stated back reading my Bible a lot with this pregnancy. Maybe it was the fact that my last two babies had died, or that I thought I was going to die. Whatever it was, I really started to call on God for help.

Reading the Bible was nothing new for me. The preacher man would make me read it every day. For this pregnancy, I worked very hard. It seemed as if the preacher man worked me even harder in the field.

I was only sixteen years-old. Every chance that I got, I read my Bible. I prayed, and prayed, and prayed. I prayed for my life. I prayed for my baby to live. I prayed for someone to come and take me out of this situation. Sometimes, I just prayed for strength to carry on.

It seemed as if the more I prayed my beatings became worse. The fact that I was pregnant never stopped him from beating on me. Actually, the preacher man told me one day, "You can hit a woman upside the head!

Even if she was pregnant!

A woman's head is the hardest part of her body!"

I didn't know what to say.

During my pregnancy, there was this one time when I thought that he had killed me. It was in the fall of 1975. The preacher man was changing a flat tire on his pick-up in front of the house.

I was outside with Bathsheba. Technically, I cannot exactly remember what I was doing. All I remember was standing on the curb one minute. Then the next minute I was laid out on the ground.

"God Dammit dumb ass!

Can't you do nothing right?

You fucking ass hole!" When I came to, I heard him yelling. I began looking around to see what he actually hit me with.

Then, as I looked to my left, I saw a Jackhammer handle lying right there. "You're such a dumbass."

I swear you ain't got no dam sense!" He continued yelling as he walked off.

Dumb ass and ass hole were his two favorite words for me. The name Linda was not in his vocabulary. Thing was that he never called me a bitch, which was weird.

So, anyway my head was bleeding and hurting so bad. I just wanted to die. I could not cry, because by that time, I was emotionally drained. I didn't' care anymore.

With all that I had been through. If he killed me, it would not have been a surprise. I would not have shed a tear, even at my own funeral. It was bad enough that I still can't cry for my babies that died.

Therefore, on April 16, 1976, I had given birth to another baby girl in Osceola Hospital. It was only him and me there in the hospital. My momma stayed home with Bathsheba and his son.

This was very weird for me, because my momma was always there. Well, I did not care one way or the other. All I wanted to do was have my baby.

With this pregnancy, the preacher man named her. Yep, you heard me. He even named her after his favorite aunt from Detroit. I just laid there and let him sign the paperwork.

He named her Fancy B. Gray, taking his last name. He no longer cared about what people thought. He was done hiding his little secret. The preacher man loved his kids, and was proud to have his girls.

When we brought Fancy home, the preacher man decided to come clean. We were all sitting in the living room. He walked over to my momma, stood over her, and began pointing his finger in her face.

He said to her, "I'm a tell you now!

The first baby that she had was mine!

The second baby that she had was mine!

That new baby is mine!" My momma was just sitting in the chair looking off into space.

I could see the spit flying out of his mouth. He was pointing his finger all in her face, but she did not move. "There ain't nothing that you can do about it!

Do you hear me?

Ain't nothing you gonna do about it!" My momma did not protest or even blink an eye.

I just sat there on the couch holding my baby watching in horror as he continued to threaten her. My momma turned to look at me, but I just looked down. There was nothing, I could say.

What else could she do? I mean, this man had her calling him preacher, and me calling him daddy. It used to make my skin crawl to call him daddy. We were both stuck.

People would talk, and say things like, I stole my momma's boyfriend. Everyone was so far from the truth. I was just a child. Sometimes the adults were worse that the kids.

Actually I was a little relieved when he finally admitted what he had been doing. I had little hope that maybe someone was going to step in and take me away. The more I prayed for change, the more things stayed the same.

BONDING WITH REAL MOMMA

Whenever my real momma would come around, we would talk a lot. It seems like every time she showed up, I was pregnant. She and I would sit in the backyard and talk all day. I would talk to my real momma about everything.

She was always wearing one of her pretty wigs. Whenever she talked all I saw was her red lipstick. My real momma was sharp. Stretch pants were all that I ever wore. It was easier, because my stomach was always growing.

There were chickens running around and pooping everywhere. The dogs would be barking and chasing the rooster. A goat would be eating the dirt. Our backyard was hilarious now that I think about it. There were animals everywhere.

My real momma would say, "Linda, I wish I could get you away.

Solomon said that I will have to pay if I tried to get you away." The only thing that I said was, "ok". I began to focus on the sky. "He says that he will call the police on me." I gave up.

I stopped asking my real momma to get me away. Whenever she was there, she would help me out with my babies. Actually, my real momma used to crochet Bathsheba Ann and Fancy clothes.

One of her favorite outfits was this little Poncho set. I loved when she was around, because she would do a lot for my babies. The preacher man would treat me somewhat nice to me. Instead of calling me dumb ass, he would say Linda.

He would not beat on me when she was there either. Therefore, I always wanted her around. Funny thing though, was that my real momma would always come around right before Christmas. Maybe it was because my birthday is on Christmas Eve.

Whatever the case was, it had become a habit for me to look for my real momma around Christmas time. Even though, I loved when my real momma was around. It was always like bitter sweat. The preacher man had some weird sexual demands for my real momma and me.

He would make my real momma and I go in the bedroom together. Our job was to heat up the bed before he could get in. Then he would come in the room, strip off his funky clothes and make my momma and I kiss his penis.

He had such a foul body odor. I don't think that he ever took baths, or if he did, it was very rare. Picture an overflowing garbage dumpster. Mix that smell with a dead body that has been sitting for days. His odor used to make me want to throw up in my mouth.

Truth is that we all would stink. It was like a house full of funky people. I do not think that we never really knew how bad we stunk, because the entire house stunk. I only paid attention to the smell, because of the things that the preacher man would make me do

DON'T TAKE MY BABY

Within two years later, I was pregnant again with my fifth child. At the age of eighteen, I gave birth to a nine-pound baby girl. The preacher man named her Zoe Ann Gray.

The thing about the preacher man was that he was very into the Bible. He wanted all of his kids to have biblical names. If you think about it, there is Samuel, Hezekiah, Azariah, Ezekial, and now Zoe.

I had her in Osceola Clinic, in Amarelle, Arkansas. During that time, in 1977 people were still racist. I delivered Zoe in a big room inside the hospital. There were people lying everywhere on stretchers.

I remember lying on the female table, with my feet in the stirrups. "I don't care what you all say!

That is not her baby!

That baby is too light!" I overheard this weird conversation. Thinking that I was hearing things, I sat completely still. "That is not her baby!

Look at that little girl!

Don't no black baby come out looking that light!" There was a white woman, who came from out of nowhere.

She was talking to someone else. When I caught a good glimpse of her, I wanted to laugh. She looked like a raggedy Ann doll. Her hair was red she had freckles.

Truthfully, I thought that the woman was joking or something. I knew that I had the right baby. Zoe came out of me, not anyone else. I was scared shitless because I didn't know what to do. She was making such a huge fuss. I began to get scared that she was going to take my baby away from me.

The doctor came in and gave me some Ether for the pain. He told me that it would help the pain go away, if I go to sleep. I didn't want to go to sleep. I was too scared that this woman was going to take Zoe away.

Back then, people would steal babies very quick. As I tried to go to keep my eyes open, I found that to be very hard. Before, I knew what was happening. I went to sleep.

Later I found out that Ether would take out your hair, but who was I to complain. That is how blacks, were treated in the South. Blacks in the South were given whatever the doctors wanted to give us regardless of the long-term effects.

When I woke up the next day, Zoe was still sleeping in the bassinet next to me. As I looked around that room looking for the white woman, she was nowhere around. I breathed a sigh of relief and thanked God.

FANCY & ZOE

One thing that I learned very quickly was that my babies brought joy into my life. Zoe and Fancy were so close in age, to where I would place them in the play pin together. Zoe was a baby and Fancy was like two years-old then.

My intentions were that they would play together. Boy was I soon mistaken. It seemed as though every time I would place Zoe and Fancy in the play pin and walk away. I would have to hear Zoe crying at the top of her lungs.

Once I made it back into the room. I would see Fancy sitting on the couch as if nothing happened. One day I decided to find out what was going on. Therefore, I placed Zoe and Fancy into the playpen and went to do something. However, this time I stood off to the side as if I had walked away.

Fancy hit Zoe in the face with a toy. Then once Zoe began to cry Fancy hit her with another toy to try to shut her up. I watched her jump out of the play pin, and sit on the couch as if nothing had happened.

I could not believe my eyes. As much as I wanted to be mad at her. I couldn't. It was like one of those moments where all you could do was laugh. The sad thing is that I needed that laugh. Even at an early age, my girls were making me smile, which was something that I never did.

TWO BATHSHEBA'S

Then on November 12, 1978, exactly one year and a day later I was at it again. I found myself sitting in the back seat of the preacher man's car in active labor, AGAIN. It was very cold outside, and we were heading to Osceola Hospital. We made it to the emergency room entrance just in time.

Dr. Farley was at the emergency room entrance waiting on me. The first thing I noticed was how his eyebrows were connected. It was creepy. I laid in the backseat of the car in full labor. He came out to check on me, and discovered that the head was already out.

Then my water broke as he was checking me out. Dr. Farley stated that it was too late. The baby was already coming out. Right there under the canopy at the emergency room entrance, I was giving birth.

I gave birth to my sixth child. Once again, God blessed me with another baby girl. At the age of twenty-one, I am now the mother of four girl's. The preacher man named her, Bathsheba Mag-Dalene Gray after his mother.

He said that he always wanted a daughter named after his mother. I now have two girls named Bathsheba. There was no arguing with the preacher man. Therefore, I had to think of a way to cut all of the confusion with having two kids named Bathsheba.

My oldest daughter name is Bathsheba Ann. My youngest daughter's name is Bathsheba Mag-Dalene. What I decided to do was combine my oldest daughter name. Therefore, instead of calling her just Bathsheba, we called her Sheba Ann.

CHAPTER SEVEN

MOVE TO DETROIT

During my baby making years, I continued to talk to Shiloh. We had made various different trips to Detroit, since 1973. Shiloh and I would talk about the beatings. She was horrified for me.

Every time I told her that I was pregnant, she would stress the urgency for me to get away. I would cry, and tell her that I didn't know how much longer that

I could take it. Shiloh would say that I needed to get him to move to Detroit.

His family in Detroit was not happy with what the preacher man was doing to me. I mean, those people really made me feel loved. The family that was in Detroit was all of his relatives.

They were willing to help me get away. Not even my own family was willing to get me away from the preacher man. They were my blessings in disguise. I believe that God placed them in my life for a reason.

Uncle Robert began to tell the preacher man that he would allow him to co-pastor with him, if he moved to Detroit. This was an offer, which the preacher man could not refuse. Even though, he called himself a preacher, he never actually, had a real church.

He would hold services in the living room of our house. The congregation consisted of my momma, his son, my girls, and me. Once he moved in with us, he never wanted anyone else around.

In the spring of 1979, the preacher man announced that we were moving to Detroit. I could not believe it. We were going to Detroit. The thought of possibly getting away almost made me smile.

The preacher man sold everything literally. He sold the land, the farm, the furniture. All of my momma's money was taken out of the bank. He got rid of everything.

Uncle Robert arrived to help us drive to Detroit. This was going to be a long trip with my four babies, his son, and my momma. Even though I was traveling with babies, they were good during that ten-hour drive. They slept the entire way.

When we finally made it to Detroit, it was sometime at night. His family had already gotten us a house to live in. It didn't take long for us to get moved in. Since all we had were clothes, and my trunk of toys.

The trunks of toys were the only thing, which I managed to salvage from my troubled childhood. My daddy bought those toys for me when he was alive. I kept a talking monkey, talking dolls, and my ironing board.

I kept all of those toys from my childhood. It was a good thing that I did, because my babies always had something to play with. I never had any money to buy them anything. So I had to work with what I had.

Nothing changed when we moved to Detroit. The preacher man continued to beat me. My momma's eyesight went from bad, to worse.

Then of all things, I knew that I was pregnant again with baby number seven. I strongly believed that I was pregnant with a boy. Yes this sound strange but, just hear me out first.

The preacher man would always tell me weird things. I mean like some off the wall type of stuff. Strange thing was that I would believe him. Listening was the only way that I would learn anything.

There was this one time when I was pregnant with Ezekiel. The preacher man and I were in the field picking corn. He started talking about how he knew how to make a boy, and how to make a girl.

He said to me, "Linda, if a man cum first.

Then it's always a girl.

If a woman cum first.

Then it's always a boy." The preacher man was crazy, but he was smart.

I didn't know any better, so I would just listen to him. He made me feel like whatever he did or said was right. I used to watch him read the Bible on people and do that, "Hoo doo, voo doo" stuff. I was just a child, so it didn't matter what he told me. I would believe him anyway.

Now every time the preacher man raped me. He would cum first. I actually would never cum at all. However, a month before we moved to Detroit. I tried to test his theory.

When we went to bed that night, I put my plan into action. He climbed on top of me as usual. I knew that I was going to get pregnant. Since, it had become routine for me to get pregnant after he would rape me.

While he was on top of me, I decided to cum first. I don't know what made me do that, but I did. Please don't get me wrong. I never enjoyed anything that the preacher man did to me. Personally, I can't explain my actions.

Once we got to Detroit, I never did tell the preacher man that I was pregnant. Things had gotten really bad for me. The abuse had gotten worse. The beatings were extreme. I swear, I thought that he was truly going to kill me.

It seemed as if he was miserable in Detroit. He would take all of his frustrations out on me. He was a lot more jealous and over protective. Detroit was turning out to be even more depressing than Arkansas.

The house that we were living in was a two-family flat, and we were living downstairs. There was only one bedroom, a living room, and a small kitchen. The bathroom had no shower, but at least we had a dining room.

I never could talk to anyone, unless he was around. Actually, the only person that he allowed me to talk to was Shiloh, and even that was a rarity. I was alone in a city where I knew no one.

All I had were my girls. I was determined to do everything in my power to keep us together. I would die, if that's what it took, to protect my babies.

FIRST ATTEMPT

One of the last times that he beat on me, I wanted to kill him. I wanted to blow his brains out. Think about it, I was now pregnant with my seventh child and was only twenty-one years old.

I was so scared for my life at that time. If I didn't kill him, he would kill me. It was either kill or be killed.

I was also having sick babies back to back. I was under so much stress, and that was going to kill me. Whether, it was through the birth my babies, or living in my nightmare. Mentally, I was just tired.

The thing was that even if he did not beat me to death, I was going to continue to have sick babies. I was done, I mean, I could not take it anymore. Something had to give; either that or I was going to snap.

Every time, the preacher man would look at me. I would see death in his eyes. Thing was, I didn't know if it was his death, or my own that I was seeing. I knew that it was time.

I would sneak and call Shiloh. Even though, the preacher man knew that we were friends, he never actually allowed me to talk to her. She was always ready to help me get away.

Within two weeks, since we had arrived in Detroit. His family was ready to help me get away. I was talking to Shiloh one day on the telephone, after a beating. She told me that Uncle Robert was ready to help me get away. All that I had to do was get to the church.

From day one, after I arrived in Detroit, I wanted to go to church every day. Going to church was like my paradise. I went there to forget about my life. The day that Shiloh told me to leave was during the week. The preacher man had been moody all day. I was doing everything in my power, not to piss him off.

I did not want to give him any reason, not to allow me to go to church that day. I made sure the kids were clean, fed, and did not disturb him. However, no matter what I did, he continued to get angrier by the minute.

The preacher man and I were sitting in the dining room at the table. The plan was for me to go to the evening service, and they would get me away from him. I was looking down at the table when I said, "Daddy can I go to the evening services with Shiloh"? He started sucking his teeth.

I held my head a little higher and said, "Daddy can I go to the evening services with Shiloh?" He looked at me and said, "You ain't going down there to that church tonight!"

I looked over at my babies, who were playing quietly on the couch and knew that I had to get out. I continued to beg him. "Please daddy!

Please daddy!

You don't have to go!

Just me and the Aagh!" He jumped, up and knocked me upside the head with one of those Aunt Jemima glass maple syrup bottle. I think that I blacked out, because all I remembered was he standing over me yelling, "Cry all you want to!

Say something else, and I'll hit you in the face!" I looked up at him with his fists balled up; I knew that I was going nowhere. I got back up, and sat at the table, with my head down, crying silently.

I got up made dinner for everyone. Then I washed up my babies, with the determination that I still had to get away. When he went to sleep that night, I snuck and called Shiloh to let her know what had happened.

ENOUGH!

It was a cold Sunday in April of 1979. Just one week after my first attempt to get away. We had been living in Detroit for three weeks. We all had gone to church this day. When we returned home, I pulled out my trunk of toys for my little girls to play with.

I cherished that toy trunk. I think that they were playing with my toy train or something. Whatever it was, they were really having a good time. My girls were like my angels. I don't think that they were aware of everything that was going on.

Hezekiah came in the living room, and grabbed a toy out of my trunk. He had begun to play with it. I didn't want him to touch my toys, because he got on my nerves.

Those toys were for my little girls to play with, and not for him. Anyway, I snatched my toy from his son, and as always, he went running to his father. He was crying, and telling him that I took the toy away.

The preacher man came into the living room, where I was, and began cursing at me saying, "My son can play with whatever he wanted to!

You're just a dumb ass!

You can't tell him what he can, or cannot play with!" He knocked me upside my head a couple of times and walked off.

His son picked up the toy, and continued to play with it, just as if nothing had happened. I was so pissed off that night. I was tired of him beating on me.

When we went to bed, he had sex with me as usual. Then he rolled off me, and went to sleep. My baby Bathsheba was lying on a towel next to the mattress that we slept on.

I crawled out of bed. Then I crept over to the corner of the room. He always kept his shotgun there. I picked it up and my feet carried me to where the snoring was coming from.

I already knew how to shoot a gun, because he taught me. The shotgun was always loaded. So I pointed the gun at him. My hand wouldn't keep still. I was trying to pull the trigger back. I took a deep breath and prepared myself to blow his brains out.

The blue blanket that was covering him was going up and down. Up and down. I found myself counting as I looked at his chest rise and fall. I began to pray. "Please God forgive me for what I am about to do.

I know no other way out." My heart began pounding in my chest. I aimed the gun at the preacher man's head. For some reason, my baby Bathsheba began to cry.

He began to stir in his sleep. My heart dropped. I started to shake. I put that shotgun back in the corner quicker than the speed of light.

When he woke up, he just looked at me. He gave me that evil glare, turned over, and went back to sleep. The preacher man never knew how close he was to losing his life that day.

HELP!

Shiloh came over that next day. I looked horrible. I was beat up, and fed up. I was so depressed, and I know that it was obvious, in the way I looked.

Considering, the fact that I was pregnant. I could not take it anymore. I could not take the beatings, the sexual abuse, and the dead babies anymore. I was just ready to give up.

"Linda, you need to get away. That man gone kill you! I was listening, but I wasn't listening. Her words were going in one ear, and out of the other. "Linda do you hear me?

That man gone kill you!" I just sat there crying.

Shiloh began rubbing my hand and said, "Uncle Robert has everything set-up.

This is going to be your last chance.

If you don't get out of the Church tonight...." I started crying even harder.

"Uncle Robert is not going to be able to help you get away.

There would be no one else, to help you get away," She said. Honestly, I didn't know if I should trust her or not. After all, these people were not my real family members. Then I thought about the last time I tried to get out. The preacher man damn near killed me.

Regardless, of the circumstances, I had to keep trying. Shiloh informed me, that during Sunday services, there would be a car waiting outside for me. My job was to get out of the church with my little girls. I had to do all of this, without alerting the preacher man.

I didn't know how I was going to do it. Hell, I didn't know if I was going to be able to get away. All I knew was that the unknown, was better than the known right now.

That night when I laid my babies to bed, I said a little prayer. I got down on my knees, "God please protect my girl's and me.

God, I'm tired. I need your help." My mind was racing with many ideas, at how I could possible get away. Then all of a sudden it came to me.

On Sunday, May of 1979, three weeks since moving to Detroit. My second opportunity to get away had finally arrived. I knew that this was going to be it. It was either get out today, or stay with the preacher man, forever.

I was soon learning that Detroit's weather was nothing like Arkansas. Here it is in May, and I had to put my girl's on jackets that day. Coming from the South, I was not used to this Michigan weather.

"When momma calls you, come to me," I told my girl's that before we left out the house. They all looked at me and shook their little heads up and down. I didn't know if my plan was going to work. However, I knew that I was getting out of that church with my babies.

I only put one diaper in the diaper bag and some milk for the Bathsheba. We all left the house, piled into the preacher man's car. Then we headed to Uncle Sherman's church on East Jefferson. My momma, Hezekiah, and my girl's all went inside the church.

I sat like five pews from the pulpit. We sat on the end of the pew near the side. I was so scared, because I knew that if we did not get away. He was going to kill me.

The church was not crowded that day. See it was not a large church, but for some odd reason. There were not a lot of people there. It was a church with a congregation full of his family.

The preacher man was standing at the pulpit, preaching. I don't remember what he was saying. He was looking directly at me. I don't know if it was God, but he turned his head to face the rest of the congregation.

As, I sat there listening to him, I was so scared. My stomach felt like jelly. I knew that the one time he was not going to be watching me like a hawk was when he was preaching.

"Momma, I'm bout to go.

I want you to come with me." I was whispering to my momma. She looked right at me and her eyes got big. She began to shake her head, "No!" I started putting Bathsheba's diaper bag on my shoulder.

"Momma, I'm leaving now!

I want for you to come with me." I was still trying to whisper. She shook her head, "No!"

I pleaded with her to come with me. She just continued to shake her head, "No!"

No!

No!" At that point, my heart dropped. I grabbed her hand, and held it for a brief second.

I knew that I had to leave her, but I didn't want to. It killed me to think about leaving her. There was nothing else to do, she didn't want to come. My momma was just too scared.

I got up with my baby Bathsheba and the diaper bag. Pretending to go and change her diaper. I walked to the back of the church where the bathroom was. My heart had stopped beating.

Bathsheba was in my arms, and the diaper bag was on my shoulder. I peeked outside. Holding my breath the entire time, I was finally able to exhale. I looked outside, and saw Maybelline sitting in some color Cadillac, waving to me.

I shut the door, but not all the way. Then I began the task of calling my babies to me. There was no way that I was leaving without them, period. I love my babies, and I would die before I left them.

The preacher man has always made me believe that I was his property for life. No one was ever, capable of helping me. I believed that the only way out was death.

My heart was racing a mile a minute. I began to feel like I was about to pass out. No matter how scared I was, at that moment. I knew that God would carry us out of that church.

CHAPTER EIGHT

THE GETAWAY

My four little girls were already looking at me. So I motioned for Sheba Ann to send Fancy. To my surprise, my baby walked right to me. My heart skipped a beat. I grabbed her hand and waved for Zoe to come to me.

I watched nervously, as Sheba Ann nudged Zoe, and said, "Go to momma". Zoe Looked at me, and without a second thought. She walked over and stood directly in front of me. I shivered when I heard the preacher man's voice preaching to the congregation.

There I stood with Bathsheba on my hip. Her diaper bag was still on my side. Fancy was holding my hand, and Zoe was standing in front of me sucking her thumb. We all were standing there looking at Sheba Ann, as she was refusing to come to me.

She was scared. I was scared. Boy, I didn't know what to do. I needed my baby to walk to me! I began to pray. "Please God!

Please God!

Please, please bring my baby to me!" My feet would not let me walk out of that church without all four of my girl's.

I was waving my hand to Sheba Ann whispering, "Come on!

Come on!" For what was only, maybe three minutes at best. However, it felt like hours. Sheba Ann got out of her seat, and came right over to me. I grabbed her hand. Then I looked at my momma one last time.

With all my babies by my side, I opened the door to a new life. I don't even remember walking out of that church. It was as if someone was carrying me. The next thing I remember was sitting in the backseat of an all White Cadillac.

The driver of that car was the preacher man's cousin, Maybelline. I had met Maybelline a couple of times before. Every time, that I met her she was nice to me. She was a very pretty woman. What I remember about her, is that she had some long thick hair.

I held on to my girl's for dear life. I didn't know if this was a set-up, or if this was actually my getaway. Honestly, I the only thing I knew to do was to pray. Next thing I remember was that we were pulling up to Maybelline's house.

There was a feeling of freedom that came over me. When I opened the car door it was like stepping out of darkness. I remember it was a car driving down the street. My heart began to beat so fast.

I almost did number two in my pants. Right there in front of everyone. I just knew that it was the preacher man. He was coming to kill me for taking his girl's away. When I realized it was not him. It seemed as if my bowels had rushed back into my body literally.

Maybelline lived in a two-bedroom apartment building, with her husband and two kids. The house was nice, but I didn't care too much about that. I was only concerned about, praying that the preacher man didn't find us.

I am just so thankful that Maybelline helped me out. She gave me hope. I probably would have never gotten away. Not only did she drive the getaway car. She also allowed us to stay in her house for a couple of weeks.

I could not relax. Every day I would tell myself that today is the day. Today is the day that the preacher man would find me and kill me. I always knew that he was capable of killing me, but never knew when it was going to happen.

Since I was pregnant, I was being extra cautious and careful. The preacher man didn't know that I was pregnant. For weeks, he tried to find us. He would talk to his uncle in an attempt to find us. However, Uncle Robert never told him where we were.

The preacher man was going crazy. He would go to various family member houses looking for me and my girl's. To my surprise, no one ever told him where we were.

SISTER GEE

I do not know what happened, but one day we had to move from Maybelline's house. Uncle Robert and Shiloh took us to a sister from the church house. Her name was Sister Gee.

Sister Gee was a very nice old woman. I have a lot of respect for her. She opened up her house to my girl's and me. I learned that the preacher man's family helped each other out.

Sister Gee was not ugly or cute. The thing about her was that she wasn't clean. Sister Gee lived in a three-room backhouse. The house was- infested with roaches. Regardless of how filthy the house was, that was my safe house.

Sister Gee treated my girl's as if they were her own family and I thank her for that. She was a nice woman. Her health issues slowed her down a lot. I tried to help as much as I could, but there was just so much to do.

There was this time, when Uncle Robert called the preacher man one to let him know that I was fine and so were his girls. When he answered the phone, I said, "Your girl's are safe." I was shaking like crazy.

"Linda!

When I find you, and trust me I will!

I'm gonna to kill you, for taking my girls away!" My ears began to burn and I almost dropped the phone right there.

Instead, I just handed it back to Uncle Robert. He was looking at me like say something girl. I couldn't. My mouth could not form any words.

At that point, I didn't know what to say. All I knew was that I was going to die. I didn't know when, or how. Truthfully, I didn't even know by whom. Considering, I was now living amongst all of his family members.

The good thing for me was that the preacher man didn't know anything about Detroit. He didn't know how to get around the city. Without his family telling him how to get around, the preacher man was lost.

It took almost thirty days of searching for me, before the preacher man left Detroit. He packed up all of his things including my trunk of toys and went back to Arkansas. He, my momma, and his son were gone.

NO SLEEP

The roaches in Sister Gee's house were horrible. My girl's and I would sleep on one queen size mattress in the living room. Let's just say sleep was not my friend. I had all night just to stay up to keep the roaches off them.

There was this one incident where I had all my babies in the bed with me as usual. I was sitting in the middle of them watching out for roaches, until I dozed off. When I woke up the entire bed was crawling with roaches.

Everywhere I turned, there were roaches. I mean there were baby one's, gigantic sized ones, and pregnant one's. Literally, there were generations of roaches crawling all over us.

As I began to brush the roaches off my babies they kept to coming back. The more I brushed the more they came back. "Aag...." I attempted to scream, but nothing came out of my mouth but roaches.

Seriously, I was so scared. I began to scoop my babies up and run out of the room with them two at a time. Then as I ran to Sister Gee's room, she was laughing hysterically.

I can hear her voice now, "Girl what's wrong with you!" I stood there pointing at the roaches that were crawling all over me. "Talk girl!

What's wrong wit cha!

What the cat got your tongue!" She continued to laugh. As I opened my mouth to talk, I woke up.

Now I am dreaming about roaches. I had to inspect everything that I fed my babies. So that I could make sure, there were no roaches in their food.

I started telling Shiloh about the roaches. I would tell her about how I had to stay awake to protect my babies. Uncle Robert and Shiloh agreed to help me out again.

They allowed for me and my girls to come and stay with them. I am so thankful for the help they were giving me. They were taking on a grown woman, who was pregnant, and with four kids.

1979

I was now, completely stressed out and depressed. Talk about a zombie, I had taken that term to an entirely different level. My emotions were still all over the place.

I had taken so many licks upside the head. To the point to where I still can feel them now. It is an eerie feeling that sometimes comes over me. I just cannot explain it to anybody.

No one truly understood me. Truth was I didn't even understand my own self. The only thing I knew was that I loved my girl's, and I will do anything to protect them.

I have always known that my name was Linda Ann Strong. No one could have told me anything different. That was not until Shiloh took me to apply for ADC. ADC stood for Aid to Dependent Children.

It all started like a month after I moved in with Shiloh and her family. She and I both knew that I needed my own house. I needed money and medical insurance for my girl's and me. Therefore, the only answer was to apply for ADC.

Shiloh was the one to tell me about ADC. I didn't know anything about that stuff. The only thing I knew was how to take a beating, and shut my mouth. I needed her to help me fill out the paperwork for ADC.

It was not that I could not read or write. The fact was that I only had a ninth grade education. When I was in the ninth grade, back then education was not good.

My ninth grade year was a blur. I had so much going on. It was to the point where I could barely concentrate. I was like hey, what am I supposed to learn.

School was the last thing on my mind. All I cared about was surviving. My mind was strictly on survival and trying to maintain my sanity.

So when Shiloh took me to apply for ADC. I soon discovered that my name was not my real name. I received a letter in the mail saying that my social security number did not match who I said I was.

When I read that letter, it was all so funny to me. I truly did not know how to register that information. The letter was saying that I had to show some type of paperwork proving who I am.

Not only did I have to prove who I was. I also had to prove that my girl's were actually mine. Now this time I thought that I was having a bad dream. My girl's were all that I had.

The thing was that back in Arkansas. I never had any reason to have that information. The preacher man controlled all of that stuff. Hell, I couldn't even touch the mailbox.

My girl's did not have birth certificates, or social security cards. I had no information on my little family. We had to send my information all the way back to Arkansas in order to clear up the mix up.

On all my paperwork, that my parents had for me showed my name as Linda Ann Strong. When I started school that was how my teachers taught me how to write my name. My parents never, "officially" adopted me.

My real mother just gave me to the Strong's when I was two years old. Everyone back in Arkansas knows me as Linda Ann Strong. I was just at a loss for words.

I received another letter in the mail. This letter said that the social security number that I sent in did match a Linda K. Flower. I began to get happy thinking like that has to be me.

Flower is the last name of my real mother. Therefore, Shiloh helped me fill out the proper paperwork to change my name to Linda K. Flower. I was actually happy to have that name.

I now felt like I, "officially" belonged to someone, my real mother. My new name provided me with a connection to my real momma's family. That was a joyous moment for me.

After we were able to clear up the name mix up. I soon received ADC and Focus Hope. Receiving those, benefits were such a blessing for me. I was finally able to be my own person.

REAL DADDY

The first thing I did was apply for my birth certificate. I was hoping to find out who my real father was. Maybe he signed his name on my birth certificate or something like that. Every time I would ask my real momma about my real father.

She would always say that she didn't know who he was. For years she would tell me that. So once I received my birth certificate in the mail. My heart dropped when I realized that only my real momma signed it.

Years later, I wrote my real momma a letter asking her did she know anything about who my real father was. I wanted to know. There was a part of me that was missing inside.

So my real momma wrote me back. As I read the letter it said, "Linda, when I was young, I was fast.

Your real daddy was a lot older than me.

When he found out that I was pregnant, he left Blytheville." My eyes were reading the letter faster than my brain.

I was praying for a name or something. By the time I got to the end of the letter. I had nothing. That was it. Guess I'll never know who my other half is.

Shiloh helped me get my very first apartment. It was a small two-bedroom two family flat. There was a kitchen, bathroom, living room and a dining room. The only furniture was a small black and white television with one bed.

The lack of furniture did not bother me at all, because for the first time in my entire life I was on my own. There was not anyone to tell me what to do, how to do, or when to it.

I started to play with my girl's a lot. I mean we would have a lot of fun just singing and dancing. We would make our own music. I wanted them to do all the things that I never had a chance to do.

I would buy food that we were never able to eat in Arkansas. We had chocolate ice cream, Lucky Charm's Cereal, and cheese for our eggs. I would stock my refrigerator with all types of cakes and candy. Those were the things that the preacher man didn't allow us to eat.

CHAPTER NINE

ENOCH

On Thursday October 25, 1979, I gave birth to my seventh child at Harper Hospital. Shiloh and Uncle Robert were there, and they helped me name him. My baby boy name was Enoch De'Lawrence Flower.

He was six pounds some ounces and adorable. I was so excited to have another baby boy. He was just the cutest little baby with some white blonde hair. His skin was yellow, and to tell you the truth. Enoch looked like my first son Ezekiel.

His eyes were a light brown. He had some of the chubbiest cheeks, which I loved pinching. I actually still have his one and only picture. It's a picture that was taken in the hospital.

The doctor had told me that my baby had Yellow Jaundice. They said that they couldn't circumcise him without giving him a tan first. The doctor had to place him under a heat lamp. Just so that Enoch' skin to get some color.

After about a couple of days, I was finally able to bring Enoch home. However, he stayed sick. Enoch's stomach hurt all the time. He could not eat. I felt so bad for him.

He was in so much pain. I was constantly taking him back and forward to the hospital. The doctor's couldn't tell me what was wrong. As the weeks progressed, he continued to get worse.

I began to feed him Enfamil Soybean. His little tummy couldn't even keep it down. He was throwing up everywhere and crying all the time. I mean it was so sad. The doctor's still could not tell me anything.

Every time that I took Enoch to Harper Hospital, I had a hard time looking at him. I would walk into his hospital room. Enoch would be lying in the hospital bed. He had tubes coming out of every place of his little body.

There was a clear tube coming out of his head. He had needles coming out of his little arms. He had patches on his heart. His little eyes were closed shut. There were even needles coming out of his legs. His little private part had a tube in it.

On a cold January morning, Enoch had been out of the hospital for about two weeks. I was in the kitchen getting ready to fix breakfast. I didn't have a stove. So I was using a hot plate. My girl's were in the kitchen singing and dancing as usual.

Enoch was lying in the bed sleep. I told Sheba Ann to go and check on him. She ran back into the kitchen saying, "Mama he's not moving! Mama he's not moving!" I turned to face her and said, "What?"

Sheba Ann looked frightened when she repeated, "Mama, I tried to move him and he didn't move"! I immediately ran into the bedroom. Enoch was lying very still on the bed.

I knew that my baby was dead immediately. Back in Arkansas, I had dug graves from the age of thirteen to twenty-one with the preacher man. Therefore, I knew a dead body when I saw one.

My girl's were still running around the house playing. They were clueless to what was happening to their baby brother. I was unable to cry or feel any emotion. I didn't know what to do. The only person that I knew to call was Shiloh.

"Enoch ain't moving," I told her. Shiloh asked me what I just said. "Enoch ain't moving.

I don't think he's breathing." I responded again.

"I'll be right there." Shiloh said and hung up the phone.

As soon as Shiloh and Uncle Robert got there, they called 911. When the police and the ambulance people arrived, they started working on Enoch. The ambulance driver's took Enoch out of the house and rushed him to the hospital.

While the police were there, they began to look around my apartment. They saw that my kitchen did not have a sink or a stove. There were dishes everywhere. Now that I think about it, my house was dirty.

It was a complete mess. At that time, I didn't know anything about how to keep a house. All I knew was what the preacher man told me to do. He, was not a clean man, trust me.

The police took my girls that same day. I felt like dying inside. Truthfully, I thought that I had been doing the right thing. I didn't understand what was going on.

The cops were saying things like, "Unfit, and negligence". I had never heard those words before. I was clueless as to what they were talking about. Considering my state of mind, the cops looked at me like I was a child.

My girls were happy with me. We were laughing and playing all the time. I was like a big kid with them. Never in my wildest dreams did I think that I had been neglectful.

The police took my girl's away from me to the precinct. I was at a loss for words, because they were all I had. Everything was happening so fast. To the point where, I thought that, I was dreaming.

Foster Care

Shiloh and Uncle Robert took me back to their house. I couldn't cry, or feel anything. The only thing that I was concerned about was getting my girls back.

After like a few hours later I received a phone call from the police.

"You can come and pick up your kids, Miss Flower.

We sent the bigger one to foster care." I hung up the phone and was so happy and sad all at the same time.

As soon as I told Shiloh, she was just as happy for me. She said, "Come on let's go pick 'em up"! She and I got in the car and drove to the precinct to get my babies. When we got there, I saw my girls sitting in the precinct quietly waiting on me.

The police talked to Shiloh about my situation. I do not know how she worked it out, but I am grateful for her. The only thing that I can tell you is that it was because of her, that I got my girls back.

We left the police precinct and all went back to Shiloh's house. That night Shiloh cooked a big dinner. From my understanding, although, I am not completely correct. I believe that Shiloh agreed to be my guardian. My girls and I moved back in with Shiloh and her family.

The guardian part was funny to me, since I was now twenty-one years old. However, it all made sense, because Shiloh was in her early thirties then. She was like a mother figure to me.

While all of this was going on, I didn't think about Enoch. I was spending too much time trying to get my girls back. Actually, he had not crossed my mind. Not until Shiloh received a call from the funeral home.

Yeah, I know it sounds crazy, but hey, it is the truth. You have to realize that I buried my first son already. I put him in the ground and threw the dirt on his grave. Not only that, I miscarried my other child in the front seat of the preacher man's pick-up.

Therefore, by that time, I didn't know how to feel or express my emotions. The only thing that registered in my mind was Enoch De'Lawrence Flower had in fact died. He had only lived three months.

I don't know too much of what happened to him. Shiloh did all the talking. There was no funeral, and Shiloh told me that the state buried him. I think Enoch is buried somewhere on fourteen mile rd. somewhere.

No one told me anything else about him. I never asked about him after that day. I was so concerned about getting Sheba Ann back. It wasn't that I didn't miss Enoch, because I do. There was just so much going on.

I treated his death as if I treated my other kid's death. I did not ask any questions. All I did was shut my mouth and let Shiloh do all the talking for me. She was able to file the necessary paperwork to try to get Sheba Ann back.

It was early in the morning, probably about two or three weeks later. Shiloh received a phone call from the foster care people. They told her that we could come and pick up Sheba Ann.

We picked her up from some youth home, or something like that. My heart just expanded when I saw Sheba Ann. Her face had sort of a confused look. She probably thought that I threw her away or something.

I have never been away from any of my kids. They were always with me regardless of what I was going through. When, her little eyes caught mine. It felt like needles were piercing my heart.

She ran to me, and I hugged her so tight. All I could say was, "Thank you!

Thank you God!" Both of us breathed a sigh of relief.

After I got Sheba Ann back things began to change. I no longer had my own house. There was so much going on in my head. I began to sink into a form of depression. The preacher man's family in Detroit helped me change my life.

I am finally able to cry.

For my babies that died.

It has taken so much out of me,

To relive, that part of my history.

But, God

Put the strength in my daughter,

To, write my story.

I will have one last cry.

In order to get over you're crime.

In damaging my soul

For over a lifetime.

CHAPTER TEN

FANCY OWENS

Well I finally did get on my feet just a little bit. I still had issues though, but I didn't tell anybody. No one ever asked and, I never talked about it. It seemed to me as if people just assumed that; I had gotten over what had happened to me.

Truth was I didn't forget anything that I went through. Hell, I couldn't forget. I have constant reminders of what happened to me. I felt like a weight had been lifted off my shoulders.

Things began to change for me in ways that I never would have imagined. One person, who helped me gain my independence the most, is the preacher man's cousin, Fancy Owens. My daughter Fancy is named after her.

Fancy Owens is one of the most talented people that I have ever met. She could play the piano and sing her butt off. Her favorite thing to do was play the piano. We would all love to hear her play.

You see, after Enoch died. I lived with Sister Gee and Shiloh for a couple of months a piece. I loved Sister Gee very much. It was just that I needed my own place. There were just too many roaches for me.

So one day Fancy Owens and I were talking at Uncle Sherman's church. My girls were running around playing with their cousins, in the basement. I think that the Sunday service had already ended. I was just waiting to go back to Sister Gee's house.

I had been talking about how I needed to get my own place. Fancy Owens was looking strange for a minute. Then she said, "You know what, Linda?

God told me, you can stay with me." My eyes got big. I started to get dizzy listening to her say, "You, and them girls." For a brief second, the cat had my tongue.

Fancy Owens was like a mother figure to me and my girls. I looked up to her. So when she offered for me to move in with her. That was an offer, which I could not refuse.

She had a very nice house. It was a ranch style house on the west side of Detroit. The house was painted a pretty dark bluish type of color. Her front porch looked like it stretched from one corner to the next.

PARENTING

I actually have a very funny story about the front porch. This was in the summer time of probably 1981. Now I would always sit out on the front porch and watch my girl's play. They would be having a ball with all their little cousins.

Bathsheba used to love to sit on the curve with her feet in the street. She would sit there and just watch all the kids play. Every time she would sit on the curve. Fancy Owens would tell me to stop her.

So the next day I saw Bathsheba sitting on the curve again. “Bathsheba get outta that street,” I yelled! She turned around and looked right at me. “Bathsheba get outta that street!” She was not paying me any attention.

“Linda, you betta spank her little tail! I heard Fancy Owens voice from behind me. She scared the crap out of me. “It’s dangerous for her to be sitting out there in that street!” I turned around and saw Fancy Owens standing in the doorway.

I began nodding my head up and down. I had never spanked any of my girl’s before. So I went outside to sit on the front porch. Guess what I saw? Bathsheba was sitting on the curve with her feet in the street again. “Bathsheba, get your butt off that curve!

Get out of the street," I yelled to her! I saw her little shoulders turn in my direction, but she didn't move. I grabbed her little arms, and spanked her butt. "Now go on in the house and lay down!" She ran in the door crying.

The very next day it rained. Mother Nature had turned the streets into a ghetto swimming pool. The kids wanted to go out into the street and play. I saw Bathsheba ease her way outside onto the porch.

All I saw was her little Polk-a-dot red dress. Everyone was calling for Bathsheba to come out and play in the water. She did not budge. "Go ahead Bathsheba, its ok.

You can play in the street," I gave her a shove.

The streets were closed because of all the water. So it was ok for her to play. "Go ahead Bathsheba.

You're not going to get in trouble." I wanted her to go out and play. All of a sudden Bathsheba placed her hand on her itty bitty hips. She had a look on her face like, "I'm not going anywhere!" My poor baby had learned her lesson about going in the street. Even if I did tell her it's ok, she was not going in the street.

Sometimes, I believe that people just did not understand me. It was ok, because I didn't understand my own self. I had been beaten everyday for no reason at all, for over half my young life. Pretty much, I was dead inside.

I would say that I lived with Fancy Owens for almost six years. Within those six years, I went through a lot of changes. One of the first changes to take place was my teeth. Remember that I told you how my teeth were horrible.

Once I moved in with Fancy Owens. My mouth started to feel like my teeth were breaking through my gums. I would never smile back then. Whenever I laughed, I always placed my hand over my mouth.

It was probably about within a year when Fancy Owens said to me, "Linda, go to the dentist, girl!

I'm tired of seeing you walking around here in pain like that!" I had been moaning and groaning all day. I was irritable, and just fussing.

So when she said that. I stopped and looked at her with a puzzled look on my face. I didn't know anything about dentist and things like that. The only thing that I knew about dentist was that everyone arrived in pain. Then everyone will leave in pain.

It was early one morning in the winter time. Fancy Owens took me to the dentist. We arrived at Dr. Golden Dental Office in downtown Detroit. Going to the dentist was something new to me. I was so scared, because I didn't know what to expect.

That particular day is still sort of a blur to me. Fancy Owens decided to wait in the lobby. There was a television out there. Everyone including the black reception girl was watching the soap opera All My Children.

Ooh wee, we loved our stories. From the hours of twelve-thirty until two o'clock, the streets were usually vacant. Everywhere you turned it looked like a scene from out of those wild, wild, west movies. Just about everyone was somewhere watching Loving, and All My Children.

However, I had to go into the exam room by myself. When I opened the door, the first thing I noticed was the tools. There were little silver hammers, and small drills, all sorts of things that I've never heard of.

My heart began pounding in my chest, just having to look at all those tools. They were sitting on what looked like a silver dinner tray. I started to run out of that door. Then all of a sudden, I heard a knock.

The voice that I heard sounded like Barry White.

"Hi, it's Dr. Hungary." He said, "Can I come in"? I shifted in the big gray chair. This chair was huge, and it had so much equipment attached to it. "Yes." I cleared my throat and placed a peppermint in my mouth.

He opened the door and I could hear the receptionist telling some little boy to sit down. "Linda Flower?" I almost got a crook in my neck, when this tall white man walked into the office. He closed the door, and I said, "Yes".

Dr. Hungary walked over to the tan counter top and picked up my ex-rays. The wrinkles on his forehead began to look like crooked highway lines. He looked at me and said, "Linda, all your teeth need to come out. They are all rotten, and there's nothing I can do."

At that time, I did not care what he had to do. All I wanted him to do was to get me out of pain. He leaned the chair all the way back, and all I saw was the white ceiling.

Without hesitation he began using a long silver needle to shoot Novocain in my gums. Dr. Hungary told me to open my mouth. I watched him put on those latex gloves, and pick up something that looked like pliers. He told me to open my mouth. I did as I was told and closed my eyes.

I began to feel this painful pulling pressure like pain in my mouth. It felt like he was trying to pull my brains from inside of my head, out through my mouth. Then all of a sudden the pain stopped.

I opened my eyes immediately only to see Dr. Hungary placing a long black tooth on the dinner tray thing. Ugh, it looked nasty. He patted me on the back and said open up we have over twenty more to go.

One by one all of my doggy teeth left my mouth. Even though, I was in so much pain. I didn't care. I just wanted them out of my mouth. By the time we left the dentist office it was late in the day.

There is this one incident that is still funny to me even to this day. When I came to Detroit, everyone thought that I was dark. So as I began to take baths more my skin began to lighten up. I would say that within over a year my color had completely changed.

"Linda?

Linda, girl what happened to you?" Fancy Owens said to me when I walked out onto the porch one day. I had just taken a bath, and put on a pretty yellow spring dress. Fancy Owens was sitting on the porch watching the kids play outside.

"You done washed all that Blytheville dirt off you, child!

"I didn't even know that you were that color!" She was cracking up. The curls in her hair were shaking all over the place. I didn't know what to say. All I could do was laugh.

I always knew that I was light, but everyone else just assumed that I was dark. Back when I was a child. My skin was always red. It wasn't until the preacher man moved in when my hygiene started changing.

Living with Fancy Owens was like going through a makeover. She would tell me, "Linda, go comb your hair, child!

Take care of yourself!

Ladies don't go out the house looking any which away!

Girl, put some curls in your hair, before you go outside the house!" She was always fussing at me about one thing or another.

Fancy also taught me how to clean up my girls and comb their hair. People be like, someone had to teach you to comb your kids hair. "Yes," yes someone did have to teach me to comb my girl's hair.

I was young myself and treated as a kid. Babies just began popping out of me every year since I was twelve years old. I didn't know anything about raising kids. All I knew was that I had four girls, and they were all mine.

With the help of Fancy Owen, I kept my girls in pretty clothes. They stayed clean and smelled good. I actually have pictures of my girls at an early age, which was something that I never had.

Taking pictures was something that my girls got used to at an early age. Every time someone pulled the camera out. They would start posing and showing off their clothes and shoes. That I bought. I felt proud.

My girls began to look good. Funny thing was that, I didn't know that my girls were actually light colored. It wasn't until they washed all of that Blytheville dirt off themselves.

Fancy Owens even helped me learn how to manage my money. I began to receive my ADC checks she taught me how to save my money. She would tell me that I should put twenty-dollars in the bank, out of every check that I received.

I had started to put up the twenty-dollars with every check. Then all of a sudden, I began to have something that I never had. I had money, and a bank account. Now, I was ready to buy my girls everything that I could afford.

Fancy Owens taught me how to manage my money. One day Fancy Owens and I were sitting on the front porch watching the kids play. I had just gotten my check and I wanted to shop. She began to talking to me.

"Linda, you need to manage your money.

You can't be out here buying everything at once. You have four kids to take care of." I sat there staring off into the sun thinking about what she said.

"Linda?

Linda, are you listening to me girl!

You need to start putting their clothes in the layaway!" It wasn't that I was not listening to her, because I was. I had just never been taught those things before.

The next time that I received my check Fancy Owens took me to Kingsway. That place was huge. When we walked inside there were racks and racks of clothes everywhere I turned. Fancy Owens took me to the children's section and I was in heaven.

We grabbed two buggies I went wild. I was throwing all type of little pretty skirt outfits in the basket. I found all types of bows and ribbons for my girl's hair. This was the first time that I had ever shopped for them.

My girls were looking so nice in their pretty little skirt outfits with the jacket. I would buy the little tights to match their outfits. Ooh, that was the most beautiful thing. They turned out to be beautiful flowers. Wow, when I think of where they came from, it was a miracle.

There was also another family who were living with Fancy Owens. It was the kid's cousin, Edna and her daughter Olivia. They had moved to Detroit from Chicago. Edna and her daughter treated me just like I was their family. So, I called them my cousins too.

EDNA

Edna was a few years older than me, and her daughter was around my girl's age. Needless to say we hit it off real quick. One thing that stood out about Edna and her daughter, were their eyes. They had some of the prettiest gray eyes.

Fancy Owens ended up buying her first house. It was a nice house in downtown Detroit. It was freshly painted an odd yellow color. The house turned out to be big enough for her to turn it into a two-family. I don't remember if Edna moved in first, or if we moved in together.

All I know is that she and I ended up living together in the upper flat. Boy, those were some good times. Edna and I began to let the kids run wild. They were able to play in the house with each other. It was just like a house full of kids.

They would fight each other sometimes, but over all they got along. Edna taught me some good things that I'll never forget. She taught me how to enjoy life and have fun with my girls.

Every time that Edna and I would get our checks we would go out to eat. All the other kids would have to go to school except Bathsheba. So we would curl our hair, and put on our pretty outfits. It was nice to get out and enjoy life.

We would all be running around the house playing, just like big ole kids. I began to laugh more and learn how to communicate with people. When I think about Edna, all I do is smile. I mean that woman brought the light into my life.

I used to follow her around so much. It was like every time you saw Edna. I was somewhere close behind. People actually began to call her, "Mother Bird". We hung together like wet clothes.

I would say that maybe three or four years after living with Fancy Owens. We moved into The Parks. The housing complex was down the street from Fancy Owens house. This time I had my own apartment again. Edna also moved in her own apartment in the same complex.

The Parks had about twelve small individual apartments that were all connected. Every apartment had one of the preacher man's family members living in it. There were cousins everywhere. We used to have some fun living in The Parks.

On hot summer nights we used to have these parties. Everyone would cook a dish and we would party through the night. One of the cousins was a DJ, and he would be playing the hits. My favorite song was Zapp's Computer Love.

I can still hear that beat in my head.

"Dum....dum....dum, dum,dum,dum.

"Dum....dum....dum, dum, dum, dum....dum...."

Then by the time the chorus comes in everyone was walking around singing, "Thanks to modern technologyeeee!

I guess I found my computer loveeeee....

Shube duwop....shube duwop....I wanna love you! Shube duwop....shube duwop....Computer Love!" Those were some good time. I still can't get the song out of my head. "Is that your face I see....on my computer screen!

Guess....I found my computer love....!" Ok, ok, ok, ok, I'm done.

There was nothing but family who lived there. Everyone watched out for the kids. Sometimes I thought that the kids had more fun than the grown-ups. We would have a ball just dancing and partying. Back then people were able to have fun without fighting.

The Parks Apartment was good for people just starting out. I had moved into a two bedroom. There was a living room and one bathroom, and it only had a shower. The kitchen was small, but I didn't care. It was all mines, and I could do what I wanted to do.

Edna and I continued to hang out. We began to party, which was something that I never did. At first I did not drink, because I had a natural high. I would get me a large twenty ounce Pepsi, and have a ball.

However, eventually I did begin to drink. Edna and I would party all night long. Walking from bar to bar. Man, we used to be so drunk. Cars used to honk at us. We would keep walking, just laughing, talking and having a good time.

We never used to have to worry about anything. Edna and I looked out for each other. She had my back, and I had hers. Then all of a sudden we met some guys. They were brothers.

The guy I met was named Bill. Bill was really cute. He was tall, dark, and handsome. No sooner after Bill and I met. I allowed him to move into my house with me and my girls. Never did I think that I was doing to them, what had been done to me.

I thought that I was doing all I can to protect my girls. I didn't pay attention to the signs. I went through some of the same things myself with their father. So it was hard for me to deal with what was right under my nose.

I want to say to my girl's that I am sorry for anything that they went through. I love them to death and tried my best to protect them. My worst nightmare was to have them experience some of the things that happened to me.

CHAPTER ELEVEN

GENESIS 50:20

"But as for you, ye thought evil against me; but God meant it unto good, to bring to pass, as it is this day, to save much people alive."

Forgiveness was not an easy road for me to go down. I held a lot of things in. For so long I lived in darkness. That darkness is what held me back. It was hard for me to see a future for myself, due to there not being a light at the end of the tunnel.

It wasn't until Tuesday, December 19, 1989, when I learned the purpose forgiving. I was living in Kenosha, Wisconsin on Fourteenth Avenue. My purpose for moving there was to be with my real mother.

I wanted to bond with my mother's side of the family. This was going to be a first for my real mother and I. We had never lived in the same house together for more than a couple days. I could tell that this was going to be a challenge for the both of us.

I also wanted my kids to meet their family on my side. They had only been around their daddy people all their lives. I love all my family in Wisconsin. They helped me out when I moved there. My girls and I were welcomed with open arms.

There was this one person that I was able to remain in contact with from my past back in Arkansas. Her name is Cousin Susie. When I was a child my momma and daddy sort of raised her. She was a lot older than me.

Actually, she was an adult back then. My parents practically raised her. I can remember my daddy built her house with his bare hands when I was little. Cousin Susie was very short for her age. She had kind of a round shape. I would say her shape looked like an orange.

Therefore, when I moved to Wisconsin she and I reconnected through my real momma. My real momma still kept in contact with a lot of people from Arkansas. Cousin Susie and I did not talk all the time. I would call her from time to time.

So on December 19, 1989, I had been cleaning up around the house. I decided to call Cousin Susie and check-up on my momma. When she picked up the phone it took her a minute to recognize my voice.

"Linda?

Linda from Blytheville!

Linda is that you?" I pushed the phone closer to my ear.

I said, "Yes, Cousin Susie, it's me." I began smiling from ear to ear. I said, "How is momma?" I heard cousin take a deep breath before saying, "Linda, I have momma here with me.

The preacher man's dead.

I had to go and get momma, because she had no one to take care of her." My heart stopped.

I fell back into the large brown sectional couch that was in my living room. My legs literally just gave out on me. I couldn't breathe. My heart was beating so fast, it had become hard for me to see straight.

I cradled the phone in my ear just to hear Cousin Susie calling my name, "Linda?

Linda?

Linda!

You there?" I started coughing up dry air.

I responded a dry, "Yes, I'm here!

What!

What!

When did happened to?" Cousin began to telling me the details.

The preacher man had begun to drink liquor, a lot. He had basically turned into an alcoholic over the years. His son had gotten older and moved away. So it only left him and my momma in the house together.

My momma was like one hundred years old at that time. She was all the way blind, and unable to get around. The preacher man and my momma lived in a wooden shack off highway sixty-one.

So, on December 8, 1989, the preacher man was trying to go into the house. Unfortunately, he passed out in the doorway of the house. My momma was unable to pull him inside, because she could not see.

The preacher man's body was literally lying in the doorway. Therefore, the next day, sometime in the afternoon, a highway patrol man spotted their door open. The patrol men immediately saw the preacher man's feet hanging out of the door.

My heart was still beating like crazy. I was just like, in a state of disbelief. I couldn't believe it. Immediately, I thought about my girls, and realized that they were outside playing. For a brief moment, I had been unaware of everything around me.

Cousin Susie was just talking away. She went on to tell me how the preacher man had been lying in the doorway for over twenty-four hours. She said that the preacher man had a heart attack, and fell out.

However, when the patrol men found him, his body was frozen. The house was trashed with dirty clothes and rotten food. There was no heat or indoor plumbing. Pretty much, the house should have been condemned.

They took my momma out of the house, because the conditions were terrible. She was barely able to walk or do anything for herself. Cousin Susie told me that she could not allow my momma to go into an old folk's home. So she agreed to take care of her.

I ended my phone call with Cousin Susie. Somehow I dropped the phone and it landed back in the cradle. My hands felt heavy as I tried to register the news that I just received. I immediately felt like I could breathe again.

My shoulders felt lighter. This was truly news that I would have never expected to get. Wow, hearing that the preacher man was now dead, at the age of sixty-eight. It brought out a mixture of emotions.

The weird thing was that I was still scared. I always feared that I would have to see him again. There was always the fear that he would show up to my door looking for me and the kids. My girls would eventually want to meet their dad. Those thoughts constantly ran through my mind.

I went to the front door, and called my girls into the house. As I watched each of them come running inside. They all went to various parts of the couch and sat down.

I took a deep breath and said, "Y'all daddy dead". Their reactions were like, "Ok". They didn't cry or shed a tear, blink an eye, or even budge. I understood why they reacted that way, but it made me sad.

It had been ten years since he was ever in their lives. During that time they all were babies. Once we finally escaped, I never talked about him again. My entire past was a complete cloud of darkness. I hoped and prayed that I would never have to see him again.

However, when I found out that the preacher man was dead. I saw his face in all of my four girls, but it was a different type of face. Their faces held the light that I had been chasing for so long. Regardless of how I felt about what the preacher man did to me. It hit me that those were his girls too.

I wanted to give them something that I never had. It was a chance to know who their real father was. At that moment in thought, I forgave him. I knew that I had to forgive him so that I could move on.

My girls knew nothing about their father. I could have told them about all the things that the preacher man put me through, but I didn't. "Girls, I don't care how your father treated me.

He always loved y'all," is what came out of my mouth.

Even though my girls still didn't understand. I wasn't about to tarnish his image in their eyes. Throughout everything the preacher man has put me through. It's not my fight anymore.

He still is the father of all my girls. I love them to death. If I were to change who their father was. Then it would change who they are. I have four beautiful flowers. I thank God everyday for them.

Throughout all the evil that was placed upon me. God turned it into good. When I began to tell my story, Forgiveness was just a word to me. However when I began to relive my story, Forgiveness became my testimony.

Dear readers,

I started writing my mom's biography in June of 2011. I completed writing her biography in August of 2011, and my release date was November 11, 2011. Actually one day before my 33rd birthday.

Writing my mom's biography was the hardest thing that I have ever had to do in my life. At one point I had to realize that it was my momma, my grandma, and my father that I was writing about.

Forgiveness is a two-way word. Sometimes you have to Forgive someone for what has been done to you. Maybe you have to Forgive yourself for what you have done to someone else. Ultimately, we need to let it go.

Thank you,

Mary Mag-Dalene

MARK 11:25

"And when you stand praying, if you hold anything against anyone, forgive them, so that your Father in heaven may forgive you your sins."